Penguin Books

Write On

Born in London in 1935, David Lodge was educated at University College, London, where he took his BA degree in 1955 and his MA in 1959. In between he did National Service in the British Army. He holds a doctorate from the University of Birmingham and then taught in the English Department from 1960 until 1987, when he retired from his chair of Modern English Literature to become a full-time writer. He retains his title of Honorary Professor of Modern English Literature at Birmingham. He held a Harkness Fellowship in the United States from 1964 to 1965, a post as visiting professor at the University of California, Berkeley, in 1969, and was Henfield Creative Fellow at the University of East Anglia in 1977. He has lectured and addressed conferences in many countries in Europe and further afield. David Lodge is a Fellow of the Royal Society of Literature.

His novels are: *The Picturegoers* (1960); *Ginger You're Barmy* (1962); *The British Museum is Falling Down* (1965); *Out of the Shelter* (1970); *Changing Places* (1975), for which he was awarded the Hawthornden Prize and the *Yorkshire Post* Fiction Prize; *How Far Can You Go?*, which was the Whitbread Book of the Year in 1980; and *Small World*, which was shortlisted for the Booker Prize in 1984 and has been adapted as a major television serial by Granada TV. He is the author of several books of literary criticism including *Language of Fiction* (1966), *The Novelist at the Crossroads* (1971), *The Modes of Modern Writing* (1977) and *Working with Structuralism* (1981), and has also edited several classic novels and anthologies of criticism. David Lodge has recently written and presented a TV documentary film about an academic conference, *Small Worlds – Big Worlds*, which was broadcast on Channel 4. He has also written a stage play and is currently working on a new novel.

David Lodge is married and has three children. He lives in Birmingham.

DAVID LODGE

Write On

Occasional Essays 1965–1985

PENGUIN BOOKS

PENGUIN BOOKS

Published by the Penguin Group
27 Wrights Lane, London W8 5TZ, England
Viking Penguin Inc., 40 West 23rd Street, New York, New York 10010, USA
Penguin Books Australia Ltd, Ringwood, Victoria, Australia
Penguin Books Canada Ltd, 2801 John Street, Markham, Ontario, Canada L3R 1B4
Penguin Books (NZ) Ltd, 182–190 Wairau Road, Auckland 10, New Zealand

Penguin Books Ltd, Registered Offices: Harmondsworth, Middlesex, England

This collection first published by Martin Secker & Warburg Ltd 1986
Published in Penguin Books 1988

Reproduced, printed and bound in Great Britain by
Hazell Watson & Viney Limited
Member of BPCC plc
Aylesbury Bucks
Filmset in Plantin

For Christopher

Contents

Foreword

All the pieces collected in this book were prompted by an invitation or impulse to "write on" something or other: a new book or an old film, an author's anniversary or a trip to a foreign country. They also witness to a compulsion, which virtually defines the professional writer, to write on, period. To go on writing, to keep the muscles of composition exercised, on whatever topic comes to hand.

The contents are divided into two sections, "Personal and Descriptive" and "Literary and Critical", but the compartments are not watertight. There are few essays in Part I that do not contain some literary allusion, and several of the essays in Part II include an element of personal anecdote or affirmation. My previous collections of essays, *The Novelist at the Crossroads* (1971) and *Working with Structuralism* (1981) belonged essentially to the discourse of academic literary criticism. Most of the pieces in this book were written for a wider audience, and although some of those in the second section employ the dreaded jargon of "structuralism", they do so, I trust, in a generally accessible manner. This book will, I hope, interest or amuse readers who know me primarily as a novelist; and indeed several of the pieces in it concern the sources or composition of my novels.

These essays and reviews are selected from a span of twenty years' occasional writing, and it hardly needs to be said that I would not in every case express myself in the same terms if I were writing today. I have silently corrected errors of fact in the original texts; I have made cuts and small stylistic changes in the interests of readability; and I have in some cases restored passages deleted on first publication because of limitations of space. But I have not attempted to revise my opinions retrospectively. Where an explicit qualification seems called for, it is stated in a postscript to the relevant article. Otherwise, the dating of each item should allow the reader to make due historical allowance for the views expressed. For instance, the somewhat defensive posture adopted in the first essay towards an older generation deemed to be prejudiced against the American way of life would now be more appropriately turned towards the young. And if I were comparing British and American fiction today, I would probably not be quite as deferential towards the latter as I was when I wrote the essay that opens Part II.

"My Joyce", commissioned for a centenary collection of essays that never appeared, and "Pillar Plant" are published here for the first time. The first publication of the other items (sometimes under different titles) was as follows: "The Bowling Alley and the Sun" in *The Southern Review* (Baton Rouge); "The People's Park and the Battle of Berkeley" in *Alta* (Birmingham University); "Memories of a Catholic Childhood", part of "The Bowling Alley and the Sun", and "Why Do I Write?" in *The Tablet*; "The Catholic Church and Cultural Life" in *The Church Now*, ed. John Cumming and Paul Burns (Gill & Macmillan); "Strictly Confidential" and "Shakin' Stevens Superstar" in *New Society*; "Don's Diary" and "The Limitations of the Movement" in *The Times Higher Education Supplement*; "Polish Notebook", "What There Is To Tell" and "Dam and Blast" in the *London Review of Books*; "Small World: An Introduction" in *The Listener*; "Anglo-American Attitudes" in *Commonweal*; "Mailer and Female" in *New Blackfriars*; "Family Romances", "Fitzgerald's Fear of the Flesh", "Bourgeois Triangles", "From a View to a Death", "Getting at the Truth" and "Readings and Lessons" in *The Times Literary Supplement*; "Suck Cess" in *The New Review*; "Structural Defects" in *The Observer*; "American English" in *The Times Educational Supplement*; "Robertson Davies and the Campus Novel" and "Life Between Covers" in *The New Republic*; "The Art of Ring Lardner" as the Introduction to *The Best of Ring Lardner* (Dent); "D. H. Lawrence" in *The Guardian*; "The Human Nature of Narrative" and "Rabbit Reviewer" in *Encounter*.

All the author's royalties from sales of this book will go to CARE (Cottage and Rural Enterprises), a registered charity that builds and maintains sheltered communities, or "villages", in which mentally handicapped adults live and work – in particular, to the appeal fund for a new CARE village to be built near Ironbridge in Shropshire. My publishers, Secker & Warburg, are donating an additional royalty to the same cause. I am very grateful to them for their generosity in this respect, and to my agents, Curtis Brown Ltd, for waiving the usual commission on their services in this instance.

Purchasers of this book may like to know a little more about CARE and its aims. It was founded in 1966 to establish rural communities for the life-long residential care of mentally handicapped adults, and has by now created six villages in various parts of England, looking after some two hundred and fifty residents.

"Life-long" is a key term for parents of the mentally handicapped. In the last two decades, social attitudes towards and provision for mentally handicapped *children* have improved spectacularly. In particular, it has been generally recognized that even persons of very limited intelligence can still be educated if enough patient and systematic stimulation is applied from infancy onwards, while the moderately handicapped can achieve a surprising degree of independence. When our son Christopher was born with Down's Syndrome in 1966 we were told by a Health Visitor that he would never learn to read or write and advised to consider placing him in a mental subnormality hospital. At nineteen, having lived at home, stimulated by family life, while attending excellent state special schools, he can plan his own television viewing from the *Radio Times* and *TV Times*, and write or type his own letters to the producers of "Dallas" and "Dynasty", offering to perform the more heroic male roles and marry the most attractive female stars. He can also travel to school and college by public transport, shop for his own records and tapes, cook his own supper, play a mean game of snooker, and swim a mile (which is nearly a mile further than his father can manage). Such feats are, as he would say (he has a creative way with language), "as easy as a doornail".

But what happens when Christopher's formal education comes to an end? Clearly he, and many youngsters like him, are capable of being taught certain work skills. In the present economic climate, however, with widespread unemployment, it is unrealistic to suppose that they will ever compete for jobs on the open market. In any case, they need continuous, if unobtrusive supervision to protect them from danger and exploitation. Parents inevitably grow old, ill, and die. Siblings acquire problems and responsibilities of their own. State provision is often excellent, but geographically variable and in the long term unpredictable.

CARE villages, and other charitable enterprises like them, offer one solution to what for many parents is the all-important question: what happens to our mentally handicapped child when we are no longer able to look after him or her? It offers an environment in which the mentally handicapped can fulfil whatever potential they have for useful work, rewarding recreation and meaningful personal relationships. Villagers enjoy the privacy of their own "bedsitters" and are given an opportunity to make a positive contribution to the community. They are engaged in an active social life and are encouraged in both work and play to develop their limited skills.

Any reader who would like to know more about CARE and its villages should write to the organization's Head Office at 9a Weir Rd, Kibworth, Leicester LE8 OLQ.

PART I

Personal and Descriptive

The Bowling Alley and the Sun (1968)

OR, HOW I LEARNED TO STOP WORRYING AND LOVE AMERICA

This is a reflective essay about my first experience of America, the opportunity for which came to me through the good fortune of being awarded a Harkness Commonwealth Fellowship in 1964–65. The essay was first written a year after my return to England, and since then I have read it through occasionally, revised this passage, tinkered with that. Now seems an appropriate moment to let it have its chance in the world; for by the time it is published I hope to have visited the United States again, and shall then inevitably begin to doubt the validity of my first impressions.

The validity claimed for them now, I hasten to add, is entirely personal. Nothing I could offer by way of factual objective description would have much interest or novelty. The America I discovered has been discovered thousands of times before: every summer deposits on the shores of the New World a fresh wave of academic Columbuses, clutching like talismans the documentary proof of their fellowships, visiting professorships, or writer-in-residenceships. I want to avoid, so far as possible, the delusion of the pushy Oxford graduate in one of John Updike's stories, who "had already been published in one of the liberal British weeklies, and . . . seemed to imagine that visiting the transatlantic land mass constituted a journalistic scoop". But to discover a foreign country is also to discover oneself; and this is always new, if not news.

What is, perhaps, in a loose sense, news, is that Englishmen who came of age since World War II have increasingly gone to America to discover themselves. In the past, the educated Englishman sought to broaden his horizons by spending a year or two in Europe – in Italy, Germany, or France. Nowadays, his education is incomplete without a year in the

States and the Grand Tour goes via New York, Chicago, and San Francisco. The reasons for this trend are obvious enough: the cultural and intellectual dominance of America since the war, its wealth of research facilities and resources, the financial rewards it can offer, and so on. One might speculate, too, that for the generation that recognized a spokesman in the author of *I Like It Here*, America has offered a means of travelling without joining the cult of Abroad. But the reasons which push the young English intellectual towards America are perhaps less interesting than what happens to him when he gets there, and how this affects him subsequently: the experience of America must test and modify his sense of his own identity, values, and possibilities. Considering the scale on which the experiment is being tried, it is a cultural phenomenon of some significance; and, if the following account has any representative interest, it will be in that respect.

Essentially, the point is this: I liked America very much, and I believe that most British visitors of my type have liked America very much. And although there are obviously and inevitably many things we haven't liked about America, we don't feel in the least superior on that account. This is something that an older generation of British intellectuals, educated in the Europe-orientated tradition, and a large number of American intellectuals, caught up in the occupational hazard of alienation, find difficult to understand. They may find what follows illuminating, though probably not edifying.

First, a word or two about the title of this essay. Early in my casual reading in American literature, I came across a poem by the seventeenth-century Metaphysical poet, Edward Taylor, the poem in praise of God's creative power which forms the preface to *God's Determinations*. It advances by a series of rhetorical questions:

> Who blew the Bellows of his Furnace Vast?
> Or held the Mould wherein the world was Cast?
> Who laid its Corner Stone? On whose Command?
> Where stand the Pillars upon which it stands?

The second line of one particular couplet stuck in my mind:

> Who Spread its Canopy? Or Curtains Spun?
> Who in this Bowling Alley bowld the Sun?

The poem is about the cosmos; but the image of the bowling alley, by an anachronistic association, made the line seem peculiarly American in reference, and, in its daring combination with Sun, to concentrate for me two salient characteristics of the American experience.

The Bowling Alley, the modern bowling alley, that curious place of popular resort and recreation, where half the fun of the simple and repetitive game lies in watching the machinery set up the pins and return the balls – this stands for everything in American life that is designed to tickle and appease our appetites as consumers, everything that seems to make the ordinary humdrum business of life require less effort and yield more pleasure than it does in England: motels and supermarkets, big cars and big refrigerators, central heating and ice cubes, showers, urban expressways, heated open-air swimming pools. And the Sun stands for itself (for one sees so much more of it in America), but also for all the natural wonders of that vast and infinitely various country. Much of the exhilaration which America yields, particularly to the visitor, derives, I think, from a tension between the Bowling Alley and the Sun. Though there is a launderette on the rim of the Grand Canyon, and the bears of Yellowstone beg for food at the roadside, there is still a sense in which America is an untamed land, palpably older than man, and apt to turn upon him in a cruel and awe-inspiring display of power – tornadoes, blizzards, floods, and droughts. One is aware of this latent power even as one cruises at a steady seventy miles an hour between one comfortable motel and the next. One has the sense of participating in a civilization which has applied technology to provide its citizens with unprecedented comforts and conveniences, but which, rather excitingly, still has only the most precarious fingerhold on the face of Nature. Curiously, urban America has created its own, grimmer, version of this drama. The streets of Manhattan are rightly called canyons – the sheer, towering walls of the skyscrapers daunt and diminish individual man as does the scenery of the Southwest; and the safe enjoyment of New York's sophisticated pleasures depends on the observance of a code of behaviour as elaborate as any wilderness-dweller's: don't walk in Central Park after dark, don't ride empty subway trains late at night, keep a chain on the door of your apartment . . .

The second part of my title refers to the fact that it was a long time before I was sufficiently able to throw off a constitutional – and perhaps national – predisposition to worry, to realize how much I was enjoying myself. My American readers, particularly Jewish ones, will no doubt scoff at any pretensions to a controlling interest in worry, but I fancy we should be disputing about two different things. The American worries about sex, politics, religion, and death – the ultimate direction of his worry is metaphysical. The Englishman is more empirical: he worries about whether he is on the right train, about how much to tip the taxi driver; he gets up in the middle of the night to see if he turned off the light in the living-room. The American is characteristically always prepared to gamble the present on the prospects of the future; the Englishman thinks the future will probably be worse.

It therefore takes a great effort of willpower for the Englishman to get himself off the ground and onto the boat or aeroplane in the first place. I well remember how my (nonacademic) neighbours in Birmingham received the news that we were going to America for a year as a matter for commiseration rather than congratulation, and how there were dark moments when I thought in my heart that they were right. In particular, I quailed at the prospect (a condition of the Fellowship) of travelling extensively in the United States for three months out of the twelve, as I was taking with me, as well as my wife, my two children, then aged four and two. Looking back, I tremble to think how close I came to passing up, on this account, one of the great experiences of my life out of sheer timidity: first by hesitating to apply for the Fellowship at all; and secondly by contemplating doing most of the three months' travelling on my own. Not only would this latter plan have been a very lonely experience for myself, and a great deprivation for my wife; it would have cost me the great sense of achievement, the enormous expansion of the frontiers of personal possibility, that came from safely and enjoyably transporting my family 15,000 miles across America and back.*

We left Providence, Rhode Island, where I had been based for the first seven months of our stay, at the end of March, and drove to California by the following route: New York, Philadelphia, Washington, Virginia, Tennessee, Kentucky, Indiana, Illinois, Missouri, Kansas, Colorado; after spending a week at the annual Conference on World Affairs at Boulder,† we headed south through the Rockies to New Mexico, then west through Arizona, Nevada, and California, where we went as far south as San Diego, before driving up the coast, via Los

* I ought to explain that the longest journey that we had undertaken with them by car, at that time, was one of 150 miles from Birmingham to South Wales, which we cautiously spread over two days. The first leg, from Birmingham to Cardiff, a distance of 90 miles, took us eleven hours and involved calls at four different garages, once entailing the removal of the entire engine. The interior of the car kept filling with grey smoke, both the children were sick, and it was raining most of the time. This is an archetypal British motoring experience, and most British motorists are haunted by it. It never troubled me in America, where one thinks nothing of driving 300 miles in a day. Having a brand-new Chevrolet helped, but more of that later.

† This uniquely American occasion really deserves an essay to itself. It is organized by a dynamic professor of sociology at the University of Colorado, Howard Higman, who every spring corrals about a hundred speakers representing various fields of interest, puts them on panels, and sets them before a largely student audience to discuss every conceivable subject, morning and afternoon, for five days, with about eight panels in action simultaneously. The quality of the discussions varies, but the sheer scale of the enterprise generates genuine intellectual excitement among both audience and participants.

Angeles, to San Francisco. The trip, which we spread over eight weeks was enormously enjoyable, educative, and surprisingly painless. The children were generally happy, healthy, and well behaved; the food and accommodation were good; and the miles slipped by effortlessly. Yet I still regarded the whole venture as a daunting and demanding challenge, and certainly never would have contemplated it if the conditions of my Fellowship had not stipulated something of the kind. But there came a day, towards the latter part of the trip, when I finally ceased to regard it as an ordeal, when I learned to stop worrying and love America.

This epiphany came, fortuitously, as such things do, in a pleasant but undistinguished little town called Kingman, in Arizona. We arrived there in the late afternoon, having driven from the Grand Canyon, where we had spent the last few days. It was the end of April and very warm. We had been enjoying warm weather for most of our trip, but it so happened that Kingman was the first town we visited where the motels had their swimming pools in operation. We duly checked in at a motel so provided and enjoyed our first, euphoric swim of the season. Thus refreshed, we went out to eat one of the best Chinese meals I have ever had. Back in the sleek, comfortable motel room, I wrote up my diary as the children slept head to toe in one of the two double beds. I wrote: "V. pleasant day. When we left Providence I looked on this trip as an arduous duty or obligation; now I see it as the vacation of a lifetime." That moment of realization not only enabled me to get the most out of our remaining months in America; it involved the preceding months in a glow of retrospective appreciation.

The point I am trying to get at is that America is a country peculiarly rich in euphoria, and one becomes more and more conscious of this the further one drives west (a British friend and I amused ourselves in California with the creation of a mythical university on the western seaboard called Euphoric State; the syllabus was to include credits for sun-bathing, surfing, and water-skiing). The emphasis I give to the hedonistic aspects of American life may seem unedifying, but I believe it looms large in most British visitors' experience. It comes out, for instance, in most of the novels about Englishmen-in-America, such as Julian Mitchell's *As Far As You Can Go*, and Malcolm Bradbury's *Stepping Westward*. It is a product of the Bowling Alley and the Sun again – a combination of great natural resources and the material means of enjoying them.

I have a certain coloured snapshot in which I can narcissistically study this euphoria. It portrays me in profile against the incomparably beautiful background of the California coast between Santa Barbara and Monterey. The green, softly contoured mountains slope down to the steep cliff-face, and the blue Pacific gleams in the sunshine. In the foreground, California poppies wave in the breeze, and in the middle distance a tiny white bridge carrying the coastal road gives an idea of the vast scale of the whole landscape. My face is tanned, my attitude relaxed – I exude health and well-being. This sense of well-being was, however, compounded not only of physical health and the enjoyment of natural beauty, but also, trivial as it may seem, of the clothes I am wearing in the picture; a tapered, button-down shirt of muted orange, blue, and grey stripes in Oxford cotton, which I bought in Gimbel's bargain basement for $1.50, and the cool, well-fitting Dacron slacks which I acquired in Palm Springs. It included things outside the picture, things like the handy little Instamatic camera that took it, the huge, fast, reliable Chevrolet (generously provided by the Fellowship) that had brought us to this peak in Darien, the picnic chest in the trunk that, packed with ice obtained from the machine in the last night's motel, kept our food fresh and inviting. It was capped by the confidence, by now taken for granted, that wherever we happened to find ourselves at the end of the day, we were sure of a clean, comfortable room, a hot shower, and a good meal attractively served. I can't think of any other place in the world – certainly not England – where *all* these ingredients could fuse to make one experience. When I looked at that picture later, from out of the shadow of an English winter, pale and jaded and feeling the draught come under the door, it seemed like a snapshot of paradise lost.

To many readers these sentiments will seem absurdly superficial and self-indulgent, unrepresentative of America and unflattering to myself. Nevertheless I will stick by them. I know America is not all like California Route 1 – I have driven through Buffalo on a late December afternoon; and I know there are millions of poor and underprivileged Americans who will never see and enjoy what I saw and enjoyed in their country. The fact remains that the kind of satisfactions I have been talking about are peculiarly American, and their easy availability is one of the things that most impresses a visitor. Almost imperceptibly, he acquires an education in the art of consumption; and this, given the nature of the modern world, is not to be despised.

As will be obvious by now, I had (*pace* Randall Jarrell) a happy heart in the supermarket; and much of the moral scorn poured upon the role of consumption in American life leaves me unmoved. If American society is materialistic, it is so in a more innocent and healthy way than the affluent democracies of Europe. Americans are enormously *acquisitive*, but they are not *possessive*. They are buying things all the time, but they are discarding things at the same rate. The European buys fewer things, and hoards them – the houses of Europe are cluttered with possessions which have long degenerated into junk. As every British visitor will gratefully acknowledge, Americans are wonderfully generous in lending or giving away all kinds of equipment, and it would be unjust to ascribe this generosity merely to their affluence. They really attach much less importance to the ownership of material goods than we do. Of course affluence comes into it, but it is more an attitude of mind. Even affluent Europeans have inherited a tradition of caution and penny-pinching which vitiates the simplest pleasures of consumption. It is built into our very institutions. Compare, for example, the American practice of having a single fare on urban public transport, a flat rate charge for telephones with unlimited local calls, and an all-inclusive price on restaurant menus, with the British practice of delicately graduated fares, accumulative charges for telephone calls and menus on which every single item of food down to the last pat of butter has its own price tag. I doubt whether the British system is any cheaper for the consumer in the long run, but it provides endless opportunities for theoretical economies, and compels him to examine his conscience before every single purchase. If the experience of America has improved my character at all, I would like to think it has made me less mean.

When I look back on my year in America, it falls into four parts: the first seven months which we spent in Providence, where I was attached to Brown University; the trip out to the West Coast; the three summer months we spent in San Francisco; and the three-week trip back to New York.

Providence was a gentle introduction to America. Old, historic, but seedy and run-down, its charming campus and the tree-lined streets of the university quarter hemmed about by tracts of decaying property, disused factories, and dull canals, Providence seemed pitched halfway between the Old World and the New. There had been some kind of compromise, one felt, between the modern American way of life and an older, more European way; and the apparatus of the former had to fit itself into the structures of the latter: discount stores are housed in the shells of disused mills; the wide, raft-like automobiles must be navigated with care through the narrow streets; and modern apartments are carved ingeniously out of the interiors of the large, high-ceilinged houses of a more spacious age. Ethnically the links with Europe are still more obvious. The population has large and identifiable Italian, Irish, and Portuguese elements, and not far from Providence there is a community that speaks only French. Our landlords were first-generation Italian immigrants, and our apartment was next door to an old Armenian shoemender.

The Providence winters are supposed to be generally damp and overcast, but ours was filled with the crisp, cold, sunny days characteristic of the rest of New England. That combination of bright sun, and cold, dry air, is particularly exhilarating to anyone used to the damp, depressing winters of the English Midlands. It is epitomized for me by the memory of a visit to Walden Pond in December. There had been an ice storm in the night, and a heavy fall of snow, but now the sun was shining brilliantly. Every leaf and twig was covered with a thick coating of crystal, and glittered in the sunlight. Every bush and tree was an inverted chandelier.

We came back again to Walden Pond in early March, to picnic with some friends. The temperature was freakishly up in the sixties, but the pond was still thickly frozen. We sat in shirt-sleeves, drinking beer and eating delicious smoked fish, while the children ran about on the ice stripped to the waist. Later, two young couples walked out to the centre of the pond, stationed themselves with deliberation in the form of a large square, and stood for a long time, apparently quite silent, black immobile silhouettes against the white expanse. What they were doing, I do not know; perhaps experimenting with the pattern of their elongated shadows, thrown across the ice by the afternoon sun. But it was almost as if they felt the occasion required some ritual recognition. It seems appropriate that two of my most vivid memories of New England should be associated with Thoreau's shrine.

We were very happy in Providence. But Providence – although it is near Boston and within easy reach of New York – is a provincial city. I didn't want to leave America without the experience of living in one of its big, cosmopolitan centres. Naturally, we chose San Francisco.

I say naturally because everyone speaks so highly of San Francisco. We thought it could never live up to our aroused expectations – but it exceeded them. San Francisco – that is where the Bowling Alley and the Sun are perfectly realized, perfectly combined.

What has preserved San Francisco from the usual fate of modern cities – strangulation by suburbia – is that, being situated on a peninsula, it can only expand in one direction. Hence, if you can contrive (as we did) to live near the end of the peninsula, you can have all the resources of a big city at your fingertips, yet by crossing the Golden Gate Bridge you can be out of the city in minutes, exploring the wooded hills and sandy beaches of Marin County. But the praises of San Francisco have been sung so many times that it is difficult to recite them without sounding like a tourists' brochure. How to convey the quality of life there – the sense of living on the very crest of a civilization, serene and poised as a surf-rider, that graced the simplest experience: riding the steep, roller-coaster hills, browsing in the City Lights

Bookshop, seeing a ship slide past the end of a city street, having tea in the Japanese Tea Gardens, watching the white sea fog creep in through the Golden Gate like a living thing, wondering idly, what shall we do this evening, shall we go and see Lenny Bruce, or hear Charlie Byrd, or have a Mexican meal, or call up some friends and invite them over?

Truly, by this time I had learned to stop worrying and love America. I made lots of friends, I called up people I hadn't been introduced to, I went cheerfully on radio and television to talk about a novel of mine (*Ginger, You're Barmy*) that had just been published, and donned headphones to answer questions phoned in by old ladies about the British Army, I did a lot of work, I smoked cigars, I spent prodigally on babysitters, I drove fast with the radio playing rock music, I bought sherry by the gallon at the supermarket and developed a taste for the rum-and-raisin ice cream you could get from a place near the Marina, the Marina where we often went on Sundays to watch the yacht racing, and where we joined in a kiteflying competition on Independence Day . . .

Then, suddenly, it was time to go home, time to turn the car east and traverse all those thousands of miles again. I suffered a temporary return of the qualms that had beset me before our westward journey, but once we were started I began to relax. Perhaps relax is the wrong word. This time we were aiming to cross the States in less than three weeks, including stops of a few days at Yosemite and Yellowstone National Parks, and at Madison and Chicago. This meant that we had to maintain a fairly high daily mileage, which lent a certain urgency and drama to the trip. By American standards it was, of course, quite leisurely; but to us it had a quality of daring and endurance. When the skyline of Manhattan finally heaved itself above the flat wasteland of New Jersey, I had the absurd feeling of having accomplished some notable feat.

It's a feeling that one scarcely gets from travelling in Europe, where indeed such an attitude to travel is entirely inappropriate. The much mocked American practice of doing Europe in ten days derives, I suspect, from a quite understandable tendency of American tourists to treat European space as if it were like American space. Of course, the two are quite different. American space is mostly empty, and lacking in human appeal. Sometimes it is very beautiful in its inhuman way, like Arizona; often it isn't even that, like Kansas, and then its only interest is how quickly you can get through it. You can't explore a state like Kansas, you would go mad if you tried, for it is all the same, flat, inscrutable, endless, resistant to human comprehension. You assert your humanity by driving across it as fast as possible. "That's Kansas," you say with satisfaction at the end of the day, and mark off another three inches of your map with a felt pencil. You couldn't do the same to Warwickshire or Provence.

Talking of maps, nothing symbolizes the difference between travelling in Europe and America more strikingly than the routes supplied by the British Automobile Association and the American Automobile Association, respectively. The British AA routes usually have trouble fitting in more than about twenty miles of twisting road on a page; there are complicated, homely directions like, "at the market square bear right, turn left at the Bricklayers' Arms, over hump-backed bridge, then take third exit at the next roundabout"; comforting landmarks such as telephone kiosks are noted at intervals of about one-and-a-half miles so that you can be sure you are on the right road. The AAA routes we found usually had about two hundred miles to the page, as often as not a dead straight line traversing an empty space, with a few towns strung out along it like lonely beads. And how small some of those towns, which look quite important on the map, turn out to be – a post office, a general store, a motel and a gas station. "Come again," they say at the gas station, without obvious irony; but how can they mistake the glazed look in our eyes, fixed on the eternal horizon, as we wait impatiently for our change?

To avoid the heat which we expected in August, we travelled early in the morning: we rose at about 3 a.m., carried the children, still asleep in sleeping-bags, to the back of the car, and set off in darkness to do our day's stint of driving before breakfast. In fact we encountered no great heat, but we kept to our plan, for it was pleasant driving quickly along empty roads with the children asleep in the back, talking quietly and sipping black coffee picked up from an all-night café, watching the dawn spread across the sky as we drove straight into the rising sun. We saw many tremendous dawns, angry red and yellow over Nevada, sad pastel shades over South Dakota. We climbed the 10,000-foot Powder River Pass over the Bighorn Mountains, Montana, in the dark; but when we got to the plateau at the top it was dawn, and as we began to descend it was like being in an aeroplane, we were looking down on the cloud cover, and the startled deer looked at us from the sides of the road. We have many such memories of the trip, unforgettable experiences all concentrated and packed together by the speed of our progress, so that one had the impression of great riches in a little room, though objectively the reverse is the case.

Speed, then, the physical conquest of physical space (air travel, though much faster, lacks the physical dimension) is the essence of American travel, the area where the Bowling Alley and the Sun confront each other most dramatically. The superhighway system, with its supply network of motels, drive-ins and gas stations, is the front line of man's struggle to subdue nature. Of course the struggle is, in a sense, over; it was fought and won by the pioneers, and we are living on the interest of their bitter and heroic endeavours. Nevertheless there is a mythic dimension, a sense of adventure, to be found in transcontinental travel even today; and it is possible to feel imaginatively some vestiges of the awe, helplessness and panic that must have occasionally subdued the spirits of the early pioneers, lost on the endless prairies. Perhaps the modern American's concern for speed and mobility is a way of exorcizing those feelings. By keeping on the move you create the illusion of a destination. Vladimir Nabokov, supreme poet of modern American tourism, seems to be expressing some such thought when the narrator of *Lolita* says, "By putting the geography of the United States into motion, I did my best for hours on end to give [Lolita] the impression of going places, of rolling on to some definite destination, to some unusual delight."

For us, having a destination was no problem. As we pushed further east, our mileage crept up, and once we got onto the turnpike system at Chicago we did four hundred miles a day, as if England, like a tiny magnet, were beginning to exert a little more force the nearer we got to it.

*

England. It wouldn't be the same, would it? After all, there had been a change of Government since we left. It said in *Newsweek* that two hundred British shipbuilders walked out the other day because they were forbidden to make tea with water from the ship's boilers, but that was just *Newsweek*, wasn't it? American journalists loved it when England lived up to its stereotypes. But those stereotypes never were true, anyway, were they? Were they?

"I shouldn't imagine there was any need to change this evening, should you?"

An unmistakably British voice cuts through the babble of French and American accents at the great bar of the *France*, as Long Island slides past the windows. The voice of the public school, the officers' mess, the London club. Addressing me.

"No," I assure him, surveying his navy-blue blazer, dark flannels, white shirt and club tie.

"I remember, coming over, on the first evening it was a pretty scruffy show, sartorially."

"Mmmm."

Is he real? I listen mesmerized to that resonant, clipped voice, that one had imagined Jimmy Porter had silenced for ever.

"Frightfully hot in Washington. Rather embarrassing really. I was absolutely melting most of the time, but I simply refuse to walk about a capital city without a suit."

"Quite," I mumble. "Oh quite."

Will I feel a pang at the sight of English soil, I wonder? In the event it is more of a shiver than a pang, for it is raining hard at Southampton when we dock early in the morning. The immigration officials are late arriving to check passports, and we are behind schedule when we step ashore. We are disconcerted to pass, on the way, our baggage still heaped on the decks of the *France*, guarded by moody sailors. Evidently there are no dockers about to receive it. We scuttle across the wet railway lines and into the waiting-room that adjoins the customs shed. Various theories are circulating about the delay of the baggage. A barmaid volunteers the opinion that the dockers are on strike. An AA official believes that it is their breakfast hour. Several dockers are to be seen mingling with the passengers at the bar. Of course, I remind myself patriotically, Britain isn't the only country with labour problems. But is there any other country, I wonder, where you can't discover what the problem *is?* From time to time we are addressed over the loudspeaker; but the voice – the characteristic voice of British officialdom, fussy, adenoidal, using vocabulary a little above its understanding – offers no explanations. Instead it chides – there is no other word for it – chides *us* for being restless and impatient and blocking the exits. The Americans, who find it quaint to be chided, laugh and clap. The British automatically form queues for newspapers, currency, cups of tea, spread their coats on the floor and lay their children to sleep, and generally behave as though they are back in the Blitz.

At last a few men turn up on the quay and begin to receive the baggage. I take the children to watch it coming down the conveyor belt. When the trolley is full, the conveyor belt stops. (There is another trolley somewhere, but it never seems to return at the right time.) Holding a child in each hand, I watch the rain slanting down on our oldest suitcase, arrested halfway down the belt. A docker rubs his hands together, and sends me, across the gleaming railway lines, a huge, shrugging grin, as if seeking to implicate me in the two great national emotions of nothing-you-can-do-about-it and never-say-die.

"Die" seems all too likely to prove the *mot juste* a few hours later, as, squashed into a flimsy-seeming hired car, we take the narrow country lane that connects the major port of Southampton with the capital city. Occasionally, this quaint, meandering little road bifurcates into a heady stretch of dual carriageway, but I have no sooner accelerated than I am frantically braking under the urgent summons of numerous road-signs: ROAD NARROWS – SLOW – TWO-WAY TRAFFIC AHEAD – BEND – HUMP-BACKED BRIDGE. There are roads marked

CLEARWAY – NO STOPPING with bus stops on them. There are roadside cafés without parking lots sited carefully in no-parking areas. (We draw up outside one such café, next to a greengrocer's. A man comes out of the latter carrying a box of lettuces. "Is there anywhere we can park?" we ask. "We want to go to the café." He puts down his lettuces. Ah, British courtesy. "Yes," he says. "You can pull round behind there." "Round there?" "Yes, just pull round there." "Thanks." "I shouldn't go to the café, though, if I were you." "Oh? You don't recommend it?" "No, it's been closed for three months." British humour. Or is it understatement?) On, on, through the downpour. We seem to be averaging nineteen miles an hour. There's always the M1 of course. We drive up it a few days later. The trouble with the M1 is that the road can't stand up to the traffic (great stretches of it are under repair, though the repairs aren't actually going on, since it's a Saturday afternoon) and the traffic can't stand up to the road (the shoulders are littered with broken-down vehicles, and my own makes a funny noise at seventy). We could have travelled by rail, I suppose, but I'm glad we didn't. "Railwaymen: Go Slow Latest," the newspaper placards said in London. "Go Slow Latest" I like that oxymoron.

Oh yes, it takes a lot of getting used to, England. You have to re-acquire the taste for it: for the change that sprains your wrist as the conductor pours it into your hand. For five different shops for five different kinds of food. For shopping bags. For muddle. ("Yes, I can see your fuses are in," said the electricity man. "But I've been sent 'ere to put them in, so I'll 'ave to say I've put them in or I'll never 'ear the last of it. Just sign 'ere please.") For politeness where it is least needed ("*Please* tear off," it says on the tab inside the matchbox). For paying for matches. For the National Health Service. (I've been limping about on a verucca for months, determined to wait for free treatment. "Most people do it themselves," said my doctor. "Just take a razor-blade . . .") For pedestrians that prance out at oncoming cars like bull-fighters, arching their bodies as you brush past them. For houses all identical on the outside, all with different electrical sockets on the inside. Tiny, tiny houses, like cosily-furnished hen-coops. And in one such hen-coop I lie on my bed, my nose streaming, my throat itching, my eyes watering – with, in short, the common English cold.

Back.

*

I recorded those impressions of England shortly after our return, and they may give some idea of the kind of inadequacies in British life to which we had become sensitized by our experience of America. The ensuing depression was acute. As the English winter and its familiar fuel crises crept upon us, and we huddled in our cramped semidetached and realized that nothing had changed, nothing ever would change, I began to wonder whether indeed *I* had changed, or whether that year in the States had been a trance, a dream, a tantalizing vision of a kind of life, a kind of me, that had never really existed and never would exist.

"Would you like to go back?" is the question one is most often asked, and it is a fair one, particularly in view of what I have said here. Would I like to go back as a visitor? But of course! Would I like to go back indefinitely, permanently? Well . . . as I feel at the moment . . . no.

Firstly, I know that when I go back to America, nothing will seem quite as fine as it did on the first occasion – it never does. Secondly, I know that my position in America was peculiarly privileged, due to the Fellowship I held, and that it could not be sustained indefinitely, in America or anywhere else. I had no duties or responsibilities other than following my own intellectual interests. Everything I owned could be stowed in the trunk of the Chevrolet, and I could go any place, at any time, I chose. Though I took a keen interest in the issues of American domestic and foreign policy, it was a detached interest: if I settled in America I would have to take the direct impact of those huge and disturbing problems without, as an alien, being able to participate in their resolution. Thirdly, I think I would find it difficult to be a writer in America, simply because I should be cutting myself off from the experience and the audience that I understand, and taking on an experience and an audience that is strange. Finally, ruefully, I have to acknowledge a certain loyalty to my country, if it is only, in Graham Greene's words, "the loyalty we all have to unhappiness, the feeling that this is where we really belong".

The People's Park and the
Battle of Berkeley (1969)

It is something of a commonplace that the student protest movements which are an increasingly familiar feature of contemporary life are often inspired and led by militants who are committed to revolution rather than reform; who are not ultimately interested in the reasonable solution of specific issues, but who use such issues to radicalize the community of uncommitted, intelligent youth as a first stage towards overthrowing the existing social and political order. The basic strategy of such militants is to encourage demonstrations that will provoke the authorities (university administrations, the police, etc.) to an extreme display of force, thus confirming the revolutionary thesis that an allegedly democratic society is in fact totalitarian, repressive and intolerant, maintained only by violence.

In conservative eyes protest stands condemned by such an analysis, while in liberal eyes it is at least seriously compromised. But may not the thesis be so dramatically confirmed that it demands serious attention without regard to the rights and wrongs of militant strategy? That was the reflection of most observers of the events of last spring in Berkeley, California. No analysis of the kind sketched above could make the spectacle, of over two thousand heavily-armed soldiers and countless policemen forcibly suppressing the creation of a park, seem either justifiable or tolerable.

Berkeley, home of the Free Speech movement of 1964 which is often said to have sparked off a global chain-reaction of student dissidence, has, of course, witnessed many violent confrontations between students and the forces of law and order. But this time there were new and sinister features: police using shotguns, as well as clubs and tear-gas, for example. One apparently innocent person was killed, another blinded, and many injured as a result of gunshot wounds. An Army helicopter sprayed tear-gas over the campus: the gas drifted into offices, into the Cowell hospital, into the Strawberry Canyon recreation centre where faculty wives and children were swimming, into private homes south of the campus. Five hundred people were arrested on the street one morning for defying the ban on public gatherings and were made to lie face down and motionless on the asphalt of the County Prison compound for two hours. Signs appeared on walls: WELCOME TO PRAGUE. It was enough of an exaggeration to be a joke, but it was a grim joke.

It was difficult to credit that all this had happened because of a park, a little park. You would have rubbed your eyes in incredulity, if you were not already rubbing them because of tear-gas irritation. Yet in the apparent triviality of the issue lay its significance, and the reasons why it plunged Berkeley into what was probably the most serious crisis either the town or the University has faced.

The Berkeley People's Park came into being on 20 April 1969, but the history of the site must be traced back to June 1967, when the University of California Regents* approved the purchase, for $1,300,000, of the residential block bordered by the streets Haste, Bowditch and Dwight, about a quarter of a mile from the main campus. The site, then occupied by somewhat decayed housing, was scheduled for development as playing-fields, but the report which recommended the purchase also drew attention to the fact that the area "had been the scene of hippie concentration and rising crime". It is no secret that neither the University nor the Berkeley City Council looks with favour upon the hippie community which has settled, in recent years, on the fringes of the campus; and many believe that it was hostility to the hippies rather than the urgent need for playing fields which motivated the University's action. Some substance is given to this belief by subsequent events. After the property was transferred, the tenants (including many students) were evicted and the buildings razed to the ground, but nothing further was done to the site. For a year it was a mud-packed, rubbish-strewn waste lot, used only for parking. A local restaurant

* It may be helpful to explain that Berkeley is the oldest and largest of the nine campuses which, located in various parts of the State, make up the University of California. Regents are appointed by a variety of methods: but the Governor of the State (at present Ronald Reagan) is a Regent *ex officio*, and many of the other Regents are his political appointments. His views are, notoriously, right-wing on academic and other matters, and he appears to enjoy majority support on the Board. The Berkeley campus is situated in the small township or "city"of that name, part of the almost continuous conurbation that rings the Bay of San Francisco, from which it is about 12 miles distant *via* the Bay Bridge.

owner claims that he complained to the University that the site was becoming an unsightly nuisance and asked for it to be fenced off, to which the University replied that it could not afford to construct a fence. This story, if true, would be the supreme irony of the whole affair, for reasons that will become apparent.

On 20 April about two hundred students and hippies (or "street people" as they are known locally) arrived at the site and began to create what they called a "People's Park", laying down grass and planting flowers. The idea caught on – not surprisingly. No one could pretend that the Park was not an improvement on the waste lot; no one could see anything sinister in the wholly voluntary effort and contributions that were creating it. The Park, in fact, appealed equally to at least three different sections of the community: its pastoral, pleasure-giving properties appealed to the hippies, its democratic and co-operative character appealed to the New Left, and its simple amenities appealed to many (though not all) of the local residents, especially mothers and children. An almost unprecedented community spirit emerged as people of all classes and walks of life worked together on the Park and used it. Of course the rights of property were being infringed, but one could scarcely imagine a violation more innocent of greed or malice. The prescient observer might have noted that it was precisely the harmlessness and broadly based appeal of the Park that made it, from the revolutionary point of view, an ideal "issue", but nobody, I believe, anticipated or prophesied the events that followed. The property-owner, in this case, was the University, and it was therefore in the University's power to avoid a confrontation on an issue that was both trivial and emotionally loaded.

The University Administration, led by Chancellor Roger Heyns (a moderate but somewhat unimaginative man, to judge by his actions) seems to have been well aware of the potential dangers of the situation, but, in the event, failed to avoid them. There is little doubt that Heyns and his aides were under strong pressure from conservative elements in the community and among the Regents to take a hard line. Thus a familiar story unrolled of a well-meaning but weak-willed administration caught between two extreme and mutually antagonistic pressure-groups, trying hesitantly to find a compromise solution, and then being panicked into making the wrong decision at the wrong time.

On 30 April the Public Relations office of the University announced that construction of the proposed playing-field on the site of the Park was due to begin by 1 July at the latest and, in typical jargon, pointed out "the disutility of any additional labour" there. Since this was the first anyone had heard of such a timetable, it inevitably appeared as a jealous, bullying response to the appearance of the Park. The Administration did, however, try to be conciliatory. It was prepared to discuss with the representatives of the Park the development of the site to leave part of it for public recreational use, or to find alternative University land for a "park-like facility". There followed two weeks of inconclusive discussions, proposals and counter-proposals, during which the development of the People's Park continued, children's play equipment being installed, and a "People's Fish-pond" initiated. The Chancellor subsequently complained that the Park people failed to create a responsible committee with whom he could have discussions until it was "too late" – too late, presumably, for him to resist authoritarian demands for assertive action. On 13 May, he issued a fateful statement on the Park. In the course of it he shrewdly commented: "Most people are worried about a confrontation, although some people are afraid there might not be one." He correctly described the opportunity which the latter group saw in the situation: "We've got the perfect issue: the people versus the heartless University, creativity versus bureaucracy." Having thus acutely identified the trap, Chancellor Heyns proceeded to walk straight into it by announcing that "we will have to put up a fence to re-establish the conveniently forgotten fact that the field is indeed the University's, and to exclude unauthorized persons from the site".

What could be a more concrete symbol of repression than a fence (a wire fence, as it turned out, evoking associations with frontiers, prison compounds and concentration camps) around a park, an iron barrier to keep the People from their Garden? It seemed appropriate that Northrop Frye, the world's greatest exponent of archetypal criticism, was a visiting professor at Berkeley that quarter, for the whole story of the People's Park began to develop like a highly literary scenario. The fence played, rhetorically, right into the hands of the Park's defenders, as letters and articles in the student newspaper *The Daily Californian* showed, e.g. Henry Weinstein's Open Letter to Chancellor Heyns:

> After the apartments on that property were razed, the land lay barren like a swamp, used as a parking lot, until a group of *people* started to build on it, trees, shrubs, swings. *They did it with their hands, with their backs, with sweat on their brows, with love. And they named it "People's Park"*. Soon afterward you issued a statement reaffirming the University's . . . "lawful claim" over the land. Apparently a "thing of beauty can't be a joy forever" in Berkeley 1969 . . . it soon became evident that the people were not going to just get up and leave the park. So you had the police move in and had the area fenced off – with cyclone wire. Berkeley now has its own Berlin Wall, an Iron Curtain of fear and paranoia. Congratulations.

Furthermore, by laying physical claim to its property, the University enormously inflated its significance. It became Territory – a much more potent concept than property, and one which, ethnologists tell us, is at the heart of most aggression. Inevitably the supporters of the Park vowed to defend it.

At dawn on Thursday, 15 May, police surrounded the Park, evicted all and arrested some of the people who had spent the night there in defiance of the Chancellor's edict, and the San Jose Steel Co. proceeded rapidly to erect a chain-link fence at a cost of $5,000. At noon there was a rally in Sproul Plaza on the campus, in the course of which the crowd marched off to the Park to demonstrate. (The President-elect of the Students' Union, Dan Siegel, who was speaking at the time, is being prosecuted on a charge of inciting to riot.) At the Park the demonstrators were met by a large body of police. Some of the demonstrators began throwing rocks. The police retaliated with clubs, tear-gas and – to everyone's astonishment and horror – shotguns, loaded with birdshot and, in at least one case, the more lethal buckshot.

At this point it may be useful to interpolate one or two observations concerning the American police forces, specifically those in the Bay Area. Whether these policemen are particularly wicked as individuals seems doubtful. It is true that their appearance does not, on the whole, inspire confidence, but this is partly due to the intimidating uniform and paraphernalia – half-soldier, half-spaceman – which they wear. What is certain is that the corporate behaviour and code of the police is often highly discreditable – and in this community already discredited. Whereas in England (if not in Northern Ireland) it is generally assumed that a policeman will display more-than-average self-control, discipline and judgement under provocation or in situations of emergency, here the expectation is quite the reverse. Few citizens, even the most law-abiding, genuinely like, trust or respect the police. To the students, the blacks and the hippies they are simply "the pigs" (the once abusive designation has become an almost neutrally descriptive one through usage, and variations such as the "Blue Meanies" are being tried). This general attitude of fear and dislike has only hardened and embittered the police, and rendered it more difficult for anyone to bring any sweetness and light into the service. Over the past year there have been at least four major, violent confrontations in Berkeley between the police and the student/hippie population. The behaviour of the police on Thursday 15th, and the way they were armed, suggests that they were ready and eager for a showdown.

The second point is that there is a bewildering variety of law enforcement agencies in the Bay Area, who have mutual assistance pacts. Thus not only the Berkeley Police and the UC campus police were involved in the disturbance of May, but also the Alameda County Sheriffs, the San Francisco Tactical Squad, and the State Highway

Patrol. Communication between these different forces, and particularly the responsibility for orders and their execution, is often confused and ambiguous. In consequence some weeks passed before it was officially established which forces were using shotguns on Thursday 15th, and with whose authority; though few people in fact doubted that the responsibility lay with the Alameda County Sheriffs and their Chief, Frank Madigan, who for some time has been a principal villain in student mythology.

On Thursday, 15 May, I came out of the Golden Bear Restaurant on the Berkeley Campus at about 1.30 p.m., having spent lunch in agreeable discussion of phenomenological criticism with a colleague, and noticed that the nearby entrance to the campus at the junction of Bancroft and Telegraph was blocked by a large and excited crowd (life at Berkeley is full of these rapid transitions). We climbed to the balcony of the Union building and looked down the length of Telegraph Avenue, the main thoroughfare of the student quarter. It had been cleared of traffic and pedestrians for most of its length. Far down, at the junction with Haste, near the Park, there was a cloud of smoke or gas. Nearer to where we stood, the street was blocked by a large crowd that was being slowly rolled back by the police, using tear-gas grenades and baton-charges.

We returned to the English department in nearby Wheeler Hall, from the windows of which I saw, shortly afterwards, that the police, having cleared the public streets, had invaded the campus and were driving the students (some of whom were throwing stones) before them. Tear-gas grenades bounced across the plaza between Wheeler and Dwinelle halls and exploded. Young men stripped to the waist and girls in summer dresses, sunbathing on adjoining lawns, stared incredulously as the battle flowed past them, then in ones and twos moved slowly away – thus showing prudence as well as sangfroid, for any untoward gesture converts a bystander into a demonstrator in the eyes of the police. A young man poking at a gas capsule with a stick was chased, beaten and dragged off under arrest as I watched.

Slightly sickened by this spectacle (there is something ignoble about watching violence from a safe vantage point – one feels like the ancient kings who watched their set battles from the tops of specially constructed towers) I went off to meet a "Creative Writing" class. Concentration was difficult: it was like trying to hold a seminar on a battlefield. It seemed to me that the detonations of what I took to be gas grenades were extraordinarily loud and frequent: it was only later, after I had dismissed the class early, that I learned the police had been using shotguns, chasing groups of students more or less indiscriminately through the campus.

Earlier that afternoon, when the police were clearing the streets around the Park, a young man called James Rector, a visitor from San Jose, climbed to the roof of a building to escape the tear-gas inside. From a roof two houses away someone threw a rock at the police in the street below. A policeman looked up, aimed his shotgun at Rector and shot him in the stomach and chest. After a considerable delay and (according to witnesses) with no co-operation from the police, he was taken to hospital and operated upon. Three *buckshot* pellets were removed from his body. He died, rather suddenly and unexpectedly, late on Sunday night. The People's Park had acquired its first martyr (soon there was a movement to rename it the James Rector Park).

Meanwhile, the supporters of the Park had been active over the weekend. Groups of demonstrators led police and National Guardsmen something of a dance, parading through the downtown shopping area on Saturday with the (partly successful) aim of politicizing the commercial section of the town by discouraging shoppers. The demonstrators displayed a certain imaginative flair in exploiting the theme of their cause by planting flowers on vacant lots along their route, creating miniature satellites of the People's Park. Photographs appeared in the press of perspiring and somewhat sheepish policemen uprooting these offending *flora*, which were subsequently arrested and taken away in paddywagons. Another story with a humorous note concerned a pretty girl who offered fruit to thirsty National Guardsmen: it was gratefully accepted, but proved to be spiked with LSD.

The National Guard had been sent to Berkeley by Governor Reagan, at the request of the Mayor of Berkeley, early on Friday morning. Reagan was undoubtedly glad to co-operate, for he is currently making great political capital out of a hard-line policy towards student unrest. At the same time Reagan issued a somewhat vaguely defined ban on public assemblies (which was challenged in the courts as unconstitutional by the American Civil Liberties Union). The National Guard is a kind of Territorial Army composed of part-time volunteers who can be called out for duty at short notice. Many of them are young men who have chosen this form of military service as an alternative to the ordinary draft. At first their presence in Berkeley was generally welcomed, even by the demonstrators, who recognized that the Guardsmen's superior discipline and detachment from local issues offered themselves a certain protection from the police. Students fraternized with the Guardsmen, attempting to "convert" them, and they received favourable treatment in the student press (it was reported, for instance, that the detachment bivouacked in the People's Park were surreptitiously watering the flowers). But as the scale of the Guard's numbers and equipment became apparent, as their appearance on the streets and the campus became more intimidating, as they showed no signs of pulling out, resentment of their presence grew, reaching its peak on Tuesday 20th. Early that afternoon columns of Guardsmen with fixed bayonets began to manoeuvre around Sproul Plaza, virtually surrounding a large number of people, many of whom were going about their normal business. The troops donned gas masks and shortly afterwards a large Army helicopter made a low pass over the Plaza, spraying large quantities of powerful tear-gas. A British colleague of mine was caught by the gas on his way to class, and suffered violent vomiting as well as eye-irritation in consequence. Many other people, over a wide area, suffered discomfort and inconvenience, as related above. According to all civilian witnesses, there was no provocation for this tactic, which stunned and outraged the most seasoned veterans of Berkeley disturbances. It was afterwards reported that the gas was used on the orders of an NG officer, against the advice of the Campus Police Chief and the University Administration. But the damage – to the image of the authorities, as well as to the individuals gassed – had already been done. Photographs of the helicopter swooping past the University's Campanile, spraying clouds of gas, were splashed on the front pages of most newspapers, adding to the already vivid iconography of embattled Berkeley.

That Tuesday afternoon an angry "Ad Hoc" meeting of about two hundred and fifty faculty passed a series of motions censuring Chancellor Heyns, Governor Reagan and Sheriff Madigan for their handling of the crisis, calling for a Grand Jury investigation of the shootings of Thursday 15th, recommending the restoration in some form of the People's Park, and declaring their inability to continue to teach as long as the campus was occupied by police and military. On the following day many other groups and individuals in the University and the community made similar statements and appeals. The students held a referendum on the Park which resulted, predictably, in a vote in its favour of 12,719 to 2,175: the poll, representing more than half of the total student body, was the largest ever recorded.

On Friday, 23 May, a long and often emotional meeting of the Berkeley Academic Senate forthrightly condemned the methods of law enforcement used in the past week, but defeated a motion calling for Chancellor Heyns's resignation. It appeared that, although the majority of the teaching staff were disenchanted with Heyns, they feared that the Regents would replace him with a still less acceptable man. The most important result of the meeting was a proposed solution to the Park issue which evidently had the support of the Administration: that the part of the disputed site occupied by the People's Park should be leased to the City of Berkeley who would in turn lease it to a corporation of Park People, who would be responsible for its development and maintenance.

To succeed, this compromise plan required not only the approval of the Regents but the co-operation of the Berkeley City Council. The Regents found reasons for postponing a decision, and the focus of attention passed to the City Council, a nine-member elected body in which most shades of political opinion from Left to Right are represented. The Mayor, a moderate conservative, and several of his colleagues regarded the proposal about the Park with not unreasonable suspicion. They had no love for the hippies, and did not relish being legally involved in the constitution of the People's Park. Mayor Johnson accused the University of trying to pass on to the City a problem which it (the University) had created, and his view prevailed at a meeting of the Council. Meanwhile the Park supporters went ahead with plans for a massive march on Memorial Day, a public holiday due to fall on Friday, 6 June. Support and participation were promised from all over the State, and from places as far away as Wisconsin and New York, where planes were chartered by groups of sympathetic students. Estimates of the numbers likely to take part rose to as high as fifty thousand. Berkeley is a small place. Imagining an invasion of this size in the existing highly charged atmosphere, citizens looked forward to Memorial Day with deep foreboding.

Confirming one's recurrent sense that events were being manipulated by some ingenious script-writer, the question of whether official permission would be granted for the March was deferred until the very eve of Memorial Day. That night, Thursday 5 June, a momentous Council Meeting was held, which was broadcast, live and in its entirety, by KQED, the admirable non-commercial television network of the Bay Area. The transmission lasted for nearly six hours, and was undoubtedly the most fascinating TV programme I have ever watched. It was not only an extraordinarily interesting human spectacle; it was also – in the mere fact of delicate and controversial business being conducted in such publicity – an impressive enactment of that much-soiled concept – the "democratic way of life". It was one of the few aspects of the whole Park affair that strengthened one's respect for America (it is difficult, for instance, to imagine Birmingham City Council acting similarly in similar circumstances). The Council patiently heard evidence from about forty private citizens of every kind and opinion, from high-school students to housewives, from retired generals who might have walked out of *Dr Strangelove* to barefoot hippies who had in fact walked in off the street. The main issue was whether or not the proposed March should be allowed to take place. The Berkeley Police Chief was confronted by the organizer of the March and accused of bad faith over the matter of permits. Sensationally, the charge was supported by one of the Council's own officials. The permit was eventually granted on condition that the marchers kept to a single route, passing the Park site, but beginning and dispersing elsewhere. Then the question of whether the City should indicate its willingness to accept the University's proposal was raised again. The Mayor tried to suppress it, on the grounds that the Council had already voted on this matter. But it was put to the vote again, one member proved to have changed his mind, the motion was carried by a single vote, and the meeting broke up well after midnight amid liberal rejoicing.

In the event, the great March passed off happily without violence. The route was cordoned off with barbed wire. National Guardsmen and police stood armed at strategic points. But peaceful protest was the order of the day. Both the law-enforcement authorities and the demonstrators were aware that the March was being covered by television, and neither side wanted to incur the odium of provoking trouble. The marchers carried not rocks but flowers, or pieces of turf, which they laid down symbolically on the pavement outside the Park. When some young men broke up the pavement with pick-axes and planted a small tree, the cops smiled benignly. Young women on floats stripped to the waist and danced energetically to rock music – an indigenous form of protest derived from the night-clubs of San Francisco. Night fell on a scene of mostly harmless revelry.

When I left for England a month later, the People's Park issue was still unresolved. From my informants at Berkeley I gather that after a series of inconclusive meetings, the Regents finally decided to take a hard line against the Park, Chancellor Heyns protesting ineffectively. The site, still fenced, is to be covered with student housing and athletic facilities as soon as possible. On Bastille Day there was one last major assault on the fence by a mob armed with wire-cutters, which was driven off by the police.

Now, with the beginning of a new academic year, new issues and new campaigns have arisen, in particular the Vietnam Moratorium and the Angela Davis affair (she is a young black Philosophy instructor at Los Angeles whom the Regents are trying to dismiss under dated and discredited rules banning Communists from teaching in the University). The Park issue is not however entirely dead. The prosecution of the President of the Students' Union for his alleged part in the events of 15 May continues, and student athletes have announced their intention to boycott the new playing field on the Park site. On Hallowe'en Night another assault was mounted on the Park, and holes were cut in the fence. Obviously the fact that Park is Territory makes it the potential target for an interminable campaign of demonstration and sabotage.

In retrospect, the whole episode of the People's Park seems like a grotesque parody, in microcosm, of the Vietnam War. All the elements were there: the little piece of territory, a dispute over its control between a "Popular Front" and a legal, but unpopular government, a sudden escalation of conflict, massive "overkill" by the powerful allies of the legal government, followed by something like guerilla warfare, native partisans pitted against a clumsy military machine – the National Guardsmen whose faces looked as bewildered and unhappy as those of GIs in the TV pictures from Vietnam. The parallel was certainly not lost on the young people of Berkeley.

Memories of a Catholic Childhood (1976)

Mine was a wartime as well as a Catholic childhood between the ages of four and ten. The war meant separation from my father, who served in the RAF, and a periodic "evacuation" for my mother and me whenever bombing made London unsafe. I attended a variety of schools, ending up, while London suffered the final assault of flying bombs and rockets, as one of two boys in a class of girls at a convent school in Surrey that had waived its usual seven-year age-limit for male pupils. As a somewhat timid, bantam-weight child, I quite welcomed the escape from the ruthless rough-and-tumble of an ordinary school playground, but I was always anxious to return "home".

Home was a small modern semi in a drab nineteenth-century London suburb, mainly lower-middle-class and working-class in social composition. A good many church steeples were visible from my bedroom window, monuments to Victorian piety, but the Catholic church was a humble edifice, long, and low-roofed, that might have been mistaken for a non-conformist chapel if it had not been for the nearly life-sized tableau of the Crucifixion outside the porch. Next door to the church was an elementary school of grim architectural design overlooking two small, walled-in playgrounds that resembled prison exercise yards. In this church, during one of the quieter spells on the Home Front, I made my first communion, and in the school partook of a breakfast in which jelly and cakes figured conspicuously and, it seems to me, incongruously; but then the parish could hardly have laid on bacon and eggs in those days of points and rationing.

At some point in the war a bomb fell on the church, totally destroying the Lady Chapel, and considerably damaging the sanctuary. For some time one could walk past the shattered building and see the very altar heaped with broken beams and fallen masonry, impressive evidence of the wickedness of the Enemy (the struggle between Good and Evil, at this stage of one's life, tended to be allegorized as the struggle between the Allies and Nazi Germany). Subsequently mass was celebrated in the school hall, but the church was repaired in time for the re-introduction of Christmas midnight mass when the war – and the blackout – had come to an end.

Attendance at this mass is one of the keenest of my memories of a Catholic childhood. To be woken from the "nap" my mother insisted upon, to dress and go out with her into the cold night streets, was both excitingly novel and vaguely reminiscent of the first nights of the Blitz when we would run up the road together to a neighbour's Anderson shelter under a sky illuminated by searchlights. On the way to church we passed several pubs and, as their doors swung open, a gust of hot beery air and a burst of drunken singing beat against our cheeks, increasing one's sense of righteousness. By half-past eleven the brightly-lit church was packed and the carols began – so much more appealing than the doleful hymns ("Soul of my Saviour" and "Sweet Sacrament Divine") of an ordinary Sunday. Then the procession to the crib and the sung mass, and the short sermon wishing us all "a Happy and a . . . [pause for emphasis] *Holy* Christmas" as I yawned and leaned my head against the silky texture of my mother's fur coat and happily, drowsily anticipated the next morning's presents.

I don't think I ever felt at any other time of the year the same glad sense of belonging to a spiritual community. I am the only child of what used to be called in Catholic circles a "mixed marriage". My mother was Catholic, and my father a "non-Catholic" – as one said in those same circles implying that there was no positive form of faith outside the One True Church.

My mother was a dutiful but undemonstrative daughter of the Church. I was given a Catholic schooling, but the atmosphere of the home was not distinctively Catholic. There was no great profusion of holy pictures and statues in the house, religion was a topic rarely touched on in conversation, and there was little of the regular and complex social interaction with parish clergy and laity that is a feature of the typical large devout Catholic family. I had no brothers or sisters to reinforce the Catholic cultural code, and my friends in the same street happened not to be Catholic. The result was that as a child I always felt something of an outsider in the Church, anxious to belong, to be accepted, yet hanging back on the periphery through shyness, absence of familial pressure and inadequate grasp of the relevant codes.

I never, for instance, learned to serve at mass, as did most of my

Catholic peers. It was mooted at one time and I even had a trial or two, but I did not take to it. I fancy that the prospects of having to rise early and cycle to church to assist at weekday masses did not appeal to me, but in a more fervently Catholic environment I should no doubt have been made to persevere. In consequence I never felt really familiar and at ease with the liturgy. I was always afraid of doing something wrong if I found myself at the front of the church at mass – like going up for communion at the wrong bell or sitting down when the rest of the congregation stood up (the Latin naturally intensified my alienation until I started learning the language at school and acquired a missal). What might be called the actuarial side of Catholicism – the accumulation of indulgences against "temporal punishment" – had a certain fascination for me, and around the age of twelve or thirteen I made a few efforts to perform the "Nine Fridays" and similar devotions, but I was never confident that I had succeeded in fulfilling the conditions necessary to make the magic work.

I attended a Catholic grammar school run by a religious brotherhood. Ritual and cultural conformity to the Faith was reinforced here, of course, by the frequent prayers (a "Hail Mary" at the start of every lesson), by the tenor of school assembly, by the occasional retreats (long mornings spent pacing the grounds under the rule of silence reading depressing CTS pamphlets) and by the period of RI with which every day was supposed to begin. The quality of the religious instruction was however very poor. Memorizing and being "tested" on the Penny Catechism was the staple component, and I do not recall having any other religious textbook in the junior forms. Instruction concentrated monotonously on the commandments and the sacraments, and made little other reference to the Old and New Testaments. In the third or fourth year, I remember, we had a form teacher who insisted on giving us remedial maths in the RI periods and when we protested (finding algebra even less congenial than the catechism) he would snatch a rosary from the pocket of his cassock and shake it in the air with a triumphant grin crying: "There's your religious instruction! Saying the rosary's the only religious instruction you need!" In his other pocket he kept a short, heavy leather strap: like most Catholic schools, mine relied heavily upon corporal punishment, not only to maintain discipline but to punish academic failure.

In the sixth form, RI, like most subjects, got more interesting, but was biased heavily towards apologetics. A principal textbook was something called *The Question Box* by an American Paulist priest, which consisted of objections to the Catholic faith (many of which had never occurred to me before) followed by vigorous and dogmatic refutations, for example:

Q. Is not the Bible the only source of faith – the one means whereby the teachings of Christ have been handed down to us?
A. No, the Bible is not the only source of faith, as Luther taught in the 16th century, for without intervention of a divine, infallible teaching apostolate distinct from the Bible, we could never know with divine certainty what books constitute the inspired Scriptures, or whether the copies we possess today agree with the originals.

Pow! Another Protestant bit the dust.

From such sources, however inadequate, I began to get some idea of the systematic theological basis of Catholic belief, and to develop a respect for and fascination with its subtleties and complexities. Common sense told you, for instance, that (false) slander was a worse sin than (true) detraction, but moral theology demonstrated with impeccable logic that the reverse was the case since detraction could not be withdrawn without committing another sin (lying). Pow!

At about this time, in my sixteenth year, I joined the parish youth club to play soccer (the school game being rugby, which I loathed) and to meet girls. In this way I became more integrated into parochial life than I had ever been before. Yet at the same time, as I developed more self-confidence (or arrogance), and extended my intellectual horizons through reading, I became more critical of the Catholic "ghetto" culture that I encountered in the parish and at school, especially its suspicious hostility towards the arts. When I discovered *A Portrait of the Artist as a Young Man* I identified immediately with Stephen Daedalus, though I had neither the courage nor the urge to rebel on so spectacular a scale.

Literature, specifically the "Catholic novel" of Greene, Mauriac and others, helped me to resolve these tensions and paradoxes, by presenting authentic religious belief as something equally opposed to the materialism of the secular world and to the superficial pieties of parochial Catholicism. The idea of the sinner as a representative Christian was appealing to the adolescent mind, suggesting (in a wholly theoretical way, for I was as timid as I was innocent) that being a Catholic need not entail a life of dull, petty-bourgeois respectability. The extreme situations and exotic settings on which these writers thrived were, however, very remote from my experience; and when I came to try and write fiction for myself I domesticated their themes to the humdrum suburban-parochial milieu that I knew best.

The Catholic Church and
Cultural Life (1980)

This essay does not pretend to be anything other than a very personal and impressionistic account of its subject. First, I must define the scope of that subject. "Culture" can, of course, mean everything that is not nature, the whole reality that men construct by work and play. The specific contribution of the Catholic Church to British cultural life in this broad anthropological sense would, however, be difficult to measure, and difficult to disentangle from the contribution of the Irish as an ethnic group. I take my brief, therefore, to be high culture: the arts and sciences, education in its non-vocational aspect, intellectual life generally – what Matthew Arnold classically described as "getting to know, on the matters which most concern us, the best which has been thought and said". By "Church" I mean the institutional Church, and the activities of men and women significantly motivated by their membership of that Church, even if they act as a kind of internal opposition. Finally, I shall be commenting mainly on the situation in the United Kingdom, and especially England, since such competence as I may have to speak on this subject is limited to my own country.

Within these terms of reference, it seems to me that at the present time the Catholic Church is making little or no distinctive contribution to our cultural life. It has not always been so. The institutional Church, to be sure, has never been much concerned with high culture in these islands, and has often been positively hostile to it. Catholic bishops and priests have not, as a rule, been intellectuals – until recently they were educated in planned isolation from the main centres of academic excellence (the universities) where high culture is nourished and transmitted. They saw their main function as the pastoral care of a predominantly working-class and lower-middle-class community, who needed to be protected from the potentially disturbing influence of modern ideas in the arts and sciences, and drilled in unquestioning obedience to clerical authority. That "ghetto" Catholicism had its virtues, but openness to the benign influence of culture was not one of them. It was indeed, in Matthew Arnold's sense of the term, philistine (Arnold himself was thinking of the Protestant dissenting community in Victorian England, but as John Bossy has shown, English Catholicism is best understood, sociologically, as a form of Dissent). Its sacred art and architecture were generally in deplorable taste, its standards of liturgical performance were low, its devotional and homiletic language in the vernacular compared unfavourably with the Anglican tradition, and its interest in imaginative literature, drama and film was mainly that of censorship.

If the institutional Church has always been essentially philistine in disposition, however, it is not true to say that Catholicism has made no contribution to British cultural life. On the contrary, in nearly every generation since Catholic Emancipation, there have been Catholic artists, writers and intellectuals who have made an impact out of all proportion to their actual numbers: the Oxford Movement converts led by John Henry Newman, of whom Gerard Manley Hopkins might be regarded as the last; the Acton-Von Hügel circle of Liberal Catholics in the late nineteenth century; the Catholic artists and writers of the Decadence – Wilde, Beardsley, Dowson, Francis Thompson and many others; the Chesterbelloc in the early decades of the twentieth century; Eric Gill's Guild of Catholic Craftsmen in the inter-war years; the "Catholic novel" of Graham Greene and Evelyn Waugh in the 40s and 50s. Most of these figures were converts to Catholicism, and many of them were attracted to the Church precisely by its cultural heritage. But that cultural heritage was Continental European – or, if English, medieval. Catholicism, to most of these men, meant Dante, Aquinas, Gothic cathedrals, Renaissance painting, Baroque architecture, orchestral masses, the organic, pre-industrial society. Or else it meant the splendours and miseries of the spiritual life – dramas of sin and salvation, miracles and mysticism, still amazingly going on in the midst of the drab materialism of modern society. It had relatively little to do with, say, Rosary and Benediction on a Sunday evening at the parish church of an industrial suburb, followed by a meeting of the Legion of Mary and a whist drive organized by the Union of Catholic Mothers.

What I am suggesting is that when Catholics made a distinctive contribution to cultural life in this country in the last one hundred and fifty years, they projected an image of Catholicism as something essentially exotic and/or boldly opposed to the prevailing spirit of the native cultural tradition, whether the latter was seen as liberal-Protestant (in the nineteenth century) or secular-agnostic (in the twentieth). In this respect they were often expressing what had led them to the Church in the first place – a sense of its "difference", that continued to attract converts until quite recently. Brian Wicker, for instance, in a fascinating fragment of autobiography ("Adult Education", *The Tablet*, Education Supplement, 24 February 1979) describes how, when he was received into the Church in 1950, he felt: "One was joining something which put a strange gulf between oneself and the world as one knew it . . . I discovered there were people round about me who lived by *vows* (of poverty, celibacy, obedience) so strange and extraordinary that in meeting them I felt I was moving into another world. Until then I had thought only remote people of moral genius, like Tolstoy and Gandhi, lived by renunciations as total as that in the *modern* world. Now I found they existed in absurd places like Birmingham or Peckham Rye. One could actually meet them. What is more, the ordinary Catholic in the street lived a hidden life by which he shared, in his own way, that amazing world. For example, by being solemnly committed to attending Mass every Sunday without fail, whatever other so-called 'commitments' he might have; by not eating meat on Fridays, though the heavens fall; by actually *fasting* every so often . . ."

Brian Wicker himself subsequently became a leading figure in a new phase of the Church's contribution to British cultural life; the emergence in the 50s and 60s of what might be called a Catholic New Left. This movement brought together several different groups and interests, which eventually (as is the way of left-wing movements) quarrelled with each other and went their different ways: pacifists, nuclear disarmers, literary critics influenced by F. R. Leavis and Raymond Williams, democratic socialists, anti-Stalinist Marxists, and radical theologians. It had a strong base in the universities, especially in adult education. It was indeed essentially critical rather than creative in orientation, and recruited primarily from the educated middle and working classes (for with the 1944 Education Act the mass of Catholics had access to higher education for the first time and, to the dismay of some of the clergy, something like an educated Catholic laity began to form in the post-war period). The movement looked for spiritual and theological inspiration particularly to the English Dominicans, and *New Blackfriars*, under the editorship of Herbert McCabe, was its principal literary organ.

The significant thing about this movement was that for perhaps the first time English Catholics were making a determined bid to present Catholicism not as some kind of refuge from or alternative to a social and political order seen as irredeemably secular, but as a basis for transforming that order: not an escape from history but a positive intervention in it. The attempt was a brave one, but it failed, and the article by Brian Wicker cited above is in some respects a requiem for it – and for the challenging unworldliness of the Catholic Church he had himself joined. The advent of Pope John XXIII, and his call to *aggiornamento*, created a climate propitious to change, but in the event the need to fight the battle on two fronts simultaneously – within the Church and outside it – proved too much for the Catholic New Left. Perhaps, too, the theoretical basis of the movement was always too shallow, improvised and heterogeneous. Some of the leading figures in the movement have left the Church (or the priesthood); others have remained, but grown less vocal; some have become more conservative. In many ways the history of the Catholic New Left has reflected the general fate of radical utopian movements in the developed countries in the 60s and 70s ("Catholic Marxism" has proved a more viable development in the Third World, where it answers to more concrete and urgent socio-economic questions).

If the present situation is one in which the Catholic Church does not represent any distinctive force in the nation's cultural life, this is not because there are fewer Catholic artists and intellectuals about, but because their work is not defined, by themselves or by observers, in terms of their religious affiliation. How many know, for instance, that Michael Dummett, Wykeham Professor of Logic at Oxford, is a Catholic? Time was, such an appointment would have provoked much throwing of caps in the air by Catholics, and perhaps raising of eyebrows by non-Catholics. The present Minister for the Arts, Norman St John Stevas, is a well-known Catholic layman, but (quite properly) his policy is not seen to be in any way conditioned by his religious affiliation, any more than the policy of the Catholic Minister of Education in the preceding Government, Shirley Williams, was by hers. As for the institutional Church, it has in Cardinal Hume a leader who is probably more genuinely cultured than any since the days of Wiseman and Manning (and considerably more amiable than either of those two prelates), and the preservation of such artistic assets as the Church in England possesses, such as Westminster Cathedral and its choir, are more secure for his presence. The training of the secular clergy nowadays usually makes some kind of gesture towards "liberal studies", and through television, and the relaxation of the old prohibitions against attendance at theatres and cinemas, the clergy are more in touch with contemporary culture today than ever before. But culturally, as politically, the Church keeps a low profile; it does not speak with any distinctive voice on such subjects, as it does, for instance, in France or the Netherlands.

As a writer and critic myself, I am particularly struck by this absence in the field of contemporary literature. Mr Greene, of course, still goes on writing with amazing fertility of invention and undiminished interest in metaphysical questions; but from *A Burnt-Out Case* onwards his novels have become progressively more sceptical, ambiguous and inconclusive in their theological import. Whereas the protagonists of the novels of his middle period were saved or damned by the certainty of their religious faith, those of the later books tend to be wry, disillusioned humanists who can raise only a wistful hope in the possibility of a transcendental world of truth and justice. Muriel Spark, who began her career as a novelist under the generous patronage of Mr Greene, looked at first as if she would develop the tradition of the "Catholic novel" in her own way: the tone of *The Comforters* and *The Prime of Miss Jean Brodie* was lighter and more playful than that of the *Heart of the Matter* and *Brideshead Revisited*, but there was the same stark contrast between human folly and vanity on the one hand and the mysterious ways of God on the other. As she has gone on writing, however, Mrs Spark's stories – technically works of great originality – have become morally more ambiguous, "blacker" in their comedy, and more tolerant of egoists and opportunists who pursue their own ends with a certain style.

Both these novelists, it is perhaps worth remarking, live abroad, as does Anthony Burgess, who had a Catholic upbringing and, to judge from a recent interview with Graham Greene (*Observer*, 16 March 1980) regards himself as some kind of Catholic. None of these three writers (who would come high on anyone's list of distinguished living English novelists) seems to have any great enthusiasm for, or interest in, the practical effects of Vatican II on Catholic liturgy, devotional practice and general life-styles, both clerical and lay. Indeed, my own novel *How Far Can You Go?* (1980) is, to my knowledge, the first novel to deal directly with that phenomenon in an English context. Brian Moore's *Catholics* (1972) was a polemical fable set in the near future, deploring the demystification of liturgy and doctrine in modern Catholicism by celebrating a remote Irish outpost of resistance to it. The most popular and successful fictional works with a Catholic content in recent years have both been broadly comic, more or less nostalgic treatments of pre-conciliar Catholicism: Mary O'Malley's long-running play *Once a Catholic* and Neil Boyd's "Bless Me Father" stories with their TV series spin-off. It seems odd that the great British public should be tickled by these evocations of a now obsolete Catholicism; but it is less surprising that the post-conciliar Church has not provided the climate for a Catholic cultural renaissance.

The fact is that contemporary Catholicism no longer constitutes the kind of unified, sharply defined challenge to secular or Protestant values that it once did, and thus no longer provides an organizing principle or rallying-point for intellectual and artistic programmes. It is, I believe, a much more decent, humane, open-minded Christian community than it once was, but it is also rather blander, duller, and more amorphous. As a result of the upheaval of Vatican II, we have now a pluralistic kind of Church, which resembles Anglicanism much more than would have seemed possible twenty or thirty years ago, in which radicals and conservatives, demythologizing theologians and charismatics, can all find a corner to do their thing with like-minded people – who may not be Catholics at all. As I write, there is in progress an attempt by conservative forces in the Vatican to take advantage of Pope John Paul II's forceful personality and ecclesiastical conservatism to call the Church to order, and exert some of the old authoritarian discipline. They may make – they already have made – things uncomfortable for the more progressive clergy, but in my own opinion they will not succeed in reversing the general tendency of the Church towards pluralism and ecumenism – a tendency now well established in the Catholic periodical press (English Catholicism has something to pride itself on here, incidentally – I cannot think of any other Christian community in this country that produces a weekly review and two monthly reviews of the quality of the *Tablet, New Blackfriars* and the *Month*).

If I am right, the prospect of a specifically Catholic (as distinct from Christian) contribution to British cultural life and cultural debate is likely to recede still further. I cannot bring myself to feel great distress or regret at this state of affairs. I am, admittedly, biased towards the *verbal* manifestations of High Culture. Words cannot but *mean*, and meanings are always potentially subversive and threatening to orthodoxy. The fine and practical arts – music, painting, sculpture, architecture, design – are less trammelled by semantics, and have always thrived more happily in partnership with the institutional Church. It may be that practitioners of these arts would deplore more vigorously than I the philistinism of English (and Irish) Catholicism in these fields – its failure, with a few exceptions, to act as patron for the best in contemporary art. But as writer and academic, I would rather work in a pluralist secular state than in one in which the Church played a dominant or militant cultural role. History suggests that the role of the literary intellectual in the latter situation is not an easy one.

Don's Diary (1976)

The duplicated letter with which the editor of *The Times Higher Education Supplement* woos potential contributors to "Don's Diary" states that "it is one of the most popular features of the paper and is widely read". As a compulsive reader of "columns", "diaries" and "miscellanies" in newspapers and magazines I can fully credit the assertion. But why the compulsion? Why do so many of us, apparently, turn most eagerly to that part of a journal which is likely to be the most trivial and ephemeral in content?

For the same reason, I suspect, as we turn to that other unfailingly popular section of any journal, the letters page: in the hope of finding there some naked human authenticity unprotected by the conventions of writing – of, in the fashionable French jargon, an *écriture*. A vain hope, of course. Writing always conceals at least as much as it reveals, and never more, paradoxically, than when it appears to be most confessional.

The professional columnists who are so daringly unbuttoned nowadays (a lady columnist commenced her diary in one of the posh papers recently: "Monday: stayed at home this evening and shaved pubic hair") are projecting personae as artificial as those Spectators and Bickerstaffs who started it all nearly three centuries ago. The "amateurs" who contribute to such a column as this are perhaps more prone to unconscious self-betrayal, but what we betray is what we wish to be thought of, not what we are.

In the life of even the most disciplined and dedicated academic there must be days of idleness and dereliction of duty, but it would be a stunning surprise to find one in *Don's Diary*: "Monday. Intended to rise early to prepare today's teaching, but stayed up late last night watching trashy film on TV and overslept in consequence. No time for breakfast, let alone preparation. Bluffed way through tutorial at 10; 11–12, coffee and gossip in Common Room.

"Bluffed way through seminar at 12. Drank too many beers at lunch and fell asleep in chair afterwards. Late for lecture at 3. Stumbled through old dog-eared notes, almost as bored as students. Drove home with splitting headache, kicked dog and quarrelled with wife."

Somehow one cannot imagine it in the *THES*, though I daresay that in a campus novel it would not seem wildly improbable.

The fact is (I belatedly recognize) that unless one is very far down the salary scale indeed, the principal motive for writing a "Don's Diary" must be vanity, so that even self-deprecation becomes a covert bid for applause. The most characteristic stylistic feature of the genre – the omission of the personal pronoun – is a desperate but doomed attempt to disguise the essential egotism of the whole enterprise. With this discouraging reflection, I proceed as best I can.

My actual diary looks rather like a list of appointments with Great Books. This week, *The Secret Agent, Oliver Twist, Sons and Lovers, Tess of the D'Urbervilles, The Spoils of Poynton.* Next week, *Jude The Obscure,* Eliot's poetry up to *The Waste Land, The Return of the Native* Joyce's "The Dead" and Borges's *Labyrinths.*

Coming back to teaching after a term's study leave, it takes some getting used to, this breathless steeplechase over one masterpiece after another. There is no hope of properly re-reading all these books of course, especially as I am reading *Our Mutual Friend,* all 900 pages of it, for the first time in preparation for seminars a fortnight hence. Half an hour or so spent skimming through one's marked and annotated text will usually restore one's memory of it with a surprising and gratifying degree of definition.

The Spoils of Poynton I did re-read, and nearly underestimated the time required. James's style has very little redundancy: if your attention wanders and you miss one subordinate clause you are immediately lost in the maze of scruple and motive.

I suspect that the sheer volume of books that an English don is expected to hold forth about in any given week is peculiar to our subject. In one sense it is absurd; in another it is intellectually stimulating to be obliged to keep the canon of English literature rotating before one's eyes rather than filed away on the dusty shelves of fading memory.

Perhaps because of my long break – summer vacation plus study leave – I feel more than usually self-conscious of the complexity of the processes involved in small-group teaching, especially the small seminar of about a dozen students, of which I happen to be taking several at the moment.

Henry James described Fleda Vetch, the supersensitive heroine of *The Spoils of Poynton* as "a person who could think ten thoughts at once", and it seems to me that the ideal teacher ought to be similarly endowed. For one must try simultaneously to (1) learn and remember the students' names, (2) encourage them all to participate, (3) prevent any one person from dominating the discussion, (4) correct error, (5) avoid humiliating anyone, (6) make the discussion sufficiently structured for the participants to feel that they are wiser at the end of the hour than they were at the beginning, (7) follow up interesting issues that arise unexpectedly, (8) express one's own spontaneous insights if they seem valuable, (9) avoid turning the seminar into a lecture, (10) pace the discussion so that it does not peak too early or too late.

These desiderata can be divided into two categories – the social and the intellectual; and there is often a conflict of interest between them. The ideal tutorial or seminar would, I suppose, be one in which the clash of opposing views was resolved by a blinding insight into the possibility of a new synthesis, collectively arrived at in the last ten minutes, the participants reeling out of the classroom in an ecstasy of intellectual euphoria and mutual love.

In actuality most teaching falls a little short of that. For one thing it is extremely difficult, I find, to generate argument between students at the undergraduate level, because they are reluctant to appear to be undermining each other's standing in the eyes of their teacher. A kind of unspoken, instinctive pact of solidarity exists which inhibits them from arguing with each other as freely and vehemently as they do outside the classroom; so that occasionally one feels, as a teacher, rather like a soccer referee who, having blown his whistle for the kick-off, finds the players disconcertingly reluctant to make a move and is reduced to dribbling the ball himself furiously from end to end, scoring brilliant goals in undefended nets, while the motionless players look curiously on.

Strictly Confidential (1975)

In principle, a university ought to be, of all institutions, a meritocracy; but Professor Lionel Lewis* has mustered a good deal of evidence, much of it gathered piecemeal by previous investigators, to support his thesis that the evaluation and advancement of academics in American universities is not based significantly upon merit. His argument, in *Scaling the Ivory Tower*, that, although lip service is paid to "teaching ability", it is assessed in a very perfunctory and hearsay fashion, will not surprise his fellow academics. (One reason, of course, is that to assess university teaching in a systematic and open fashion would absorb so much academic time and energy as to adversely affect whatever good teaching was going on.)

More startling, perhaps, is the assertion that, outside a handful of elite universities, the often deplored threat of "publish or perish" is a myth. In the vast majority of American universities less than 10 per cent of the faculty account for more than 90 per cent of all published research. A 1970 survey revealed that almost 30 per cent of all university teachers had published no professional papers, and a similar percentage had published less than five. And on average an academic with no book to his name will achieve a full professorship only 16 months later than one with 2.5 books in print. This seems conclusive proof to Lewis that academic life is not the meritocracy he thinks it ought to be.

On the other hand, it must be said that the existence of those few universities where publish or perish *is* the rule, and where most academics would like to be if they could, has a meritocratic influence on

* L. S. Lewis, *Scaling the Ivory Tower: Merit and Its Limits in Academic Careers* (Johns Hopkins University Press, 1975).

the system as a whole. And one shudders to think of the consequences if publication were made a *sine qua non* of university tenure. It is a commonplace that there is already too much routine research in print, clogging the circulation of really original work, and Northrop Frye foresaw "a time when demands that every scholar be productive may be reversed into efforts at scholarly contraception".

The question then arises as to whether there is some concept of intellectual excellence appropriate to the academic career which is not limited to publication or teaching, though it may manifest itself in either. Lewis has looked for some such professional assessment of merit in the references that are written on behalf of applicants for university posts, but his findings are again discouraging. References tend to be most vague about purely intellectual qualifications, and excessively detailed on such matters as personality, life-style, political opinions, and physical appearance – especially where the applicant is female. On the whole he finds a marked disposition, especially in the sciences, to favour the nice guy who will not rock the boat.

As the book goes on, it becomes increasingly bitter and polemical. Lewis deplores the way the American university has developed lately – into the huge multiversity, administered by an army of bureaucrats, responsive to governmental and community pressures rather than engaged in the pursuit of intellectual excellence; and staffed by a unionized faculty that regards discrimination between colleagues on grounds of merit as invidious (as one AAUP leader memorably remarked, "prices rise for everyone, not just the meritorious"). There are many good points in his critique which deserve to be pondered by academics not only in America but in this country too. The overall effect of the book is, however, somewhat negative, because while insisting that the university must be a meritocracy to be true to itself, Lewis has nothing constructive to offer as regards the assessment of merit in an age of mass higher education. The section entitled "Difficulties in the determination of merit" is only one and a half pages long, and his own approach to the problem seems to be essentially intuitive, based on the assumption of mutual trust and shared values existing between small groups of like-minded (and high-minded) scholars.

This sounds good, but in practice it tends to produce a system which he himself very effectively criticizes – the system of "ascribed merit" and "sponsored mobility". In ordinary parlance this means that you are picked out as a bright young student and groomed for an academic career, often at your *alma mater*. As Lewis points out, this system (still widely employed at our own older universities) works against the kind of open competition that rewards merit. He dryly records that committees charged to appoint the best possible candidates in the country to full professorships at Harvard remarkably found 88 per cent of them were already at Harvard.

I confess that my confidence in Lewis's own judgement of merit was somewhat shaken by the one section of his book which deals with British universities. This is part of the discussion of academic references, and is based on a study of 57 letters written on behalf of 33 candidates for a post in the department of English language and literature.

This was the only sample Lewis was able to obtain from Britain, and he expresses some ironic amusement at the "solicitude and secrecy" surrounding such documents in this country (in the United States they seem to be scattered around as freely as confetti). Since the academic subject concerned is my own, I read Lewis's account of these letters with close attention, and I was perturbed by some of his interpretations. For instance, to support his opinion (in itself flattering to British universities) that the letters display no sexual prejudice, he invites us to:

> compare the remarks made about a female scholar who completed a study of a female literary figure with those made about a male who, even if lacking innate intuition, is still obviously qualified: ". . . a sympathetic and judicious understanding of her subject, both as a woman and as a writer"; and "The subject of his thesis was Catholic Fiction . . . and though I did not examine it I understand it was a very good piece of work. ([He], by the way, is a Catholic.)" The issue, then, is not one of sex (or religion) *per se*, but one of trusting an insider to find and recognize the truth.

Since I cannot imagine a referee in the field of English language and literature committing a tautology like "innate intuition" I must suppose that this is Lewis's judgement of the difference in quality between the two candidates, but it is difficult to see, from the words quoted, how he arrived at it. Is the "truth" in such matters so easily discerned? Consider another quotation from the letters: "His post at the British Council is not the usual job, lunching with visiting oriental professors and introducing them to various people, but is mainly concerned with teaching." Lewis cites this as an example of a characteristic stylistic device of referees: the use of an adversative "but" to conceal or minimize a "deficiency" in a candidate. "The excuses are inexhaustible," he says wearily; ". . . it would seem that with a little adroitness any failing could be discounted." But it seems to me that the example quoted is a perfectly relevant explanation, not an excuse – unless any association with the British Council is deemed an automatic disqualification for academic employment.

I must now declare a more than ordinary interest in these two instances: for I believe that they refer to the same man and that I know who he was. *I* am a Catholic, wrote my MA thesis on "Catholic Fiction since the Oxford Movement", and worked for the British Council in London in a mainly teaching capacity at the time when I was seeking my first university job.

The reader may imagine for himself the drama of this discovery – of stumbling, in the course of a reviewer's duty, upon extracts from confidential references written on one's behalf some fifteen years ago, and finding oneself accused of lacking innate intuition. I daresay that if such an experience were described in a campus novel it would be condemned as contrived and incredible. But since it actually happened, it prompts me to question the ethics of this kind of research and the manner in which it is supplied with its data. I don't like to think that the next time I write a confidential reference for someone seeking a university appointment I may be simultaneously providing the raw materials with which some future sociologist can enhance his merit.

[*Postscript:* Some weeks after this review was published in *New Society* I received a letter from Professor Lewis confirming that I did indeed figure in his sample of British references, and apologizing for any embarrassment I may have been caused. In fact, I was more amused than embarrassed by the extraordinary coincidence of my being asked to review his book.]

Polish Notebook: November 1981

These impressions of a short visit to Poland in November 1981 were written up immediately on my return to England. A few weeks later the imposition of martial law and the suppression of Solidarity filled the world's headlines. I did not attempt to revise my text in the light of these events, and it therefore acquired some unintended ironies by the time it was published in the *London Review of Books* – and, for me, considerable poignancy, since I did not know the fate of the many kind and charming people I had met in Poland. As a tiny gesture of "solidarity", I donated the *LRB*'s cheque to a charity sending food parcels to Poland. As far as I now know, the people described in these notes have survived the intervening years reasonably well. E., I am told, married a Swiss and now lives in Switzerland – of all European countries perhaps the most antithetical to Poland.

The LOT plane is late leaving Heathrow because of baggage-loading problems. "You will understand," says the ground hostess, apologizing for the delay, "that we are carrying a great deal of baggage to Poland these days." The passengers waiting at Gate 11 smile wryly at each other. Their hand luggage is bursting with goods difficult or impossible to obtain in Poland these days. The British Council has thoughtfully supplied us (British scholars bound for a conference on English literature organized by the University of Warsaw) with a list: soap, shampoo, washing powder, chocolate, sweets, batteries, notepaper, toilet paper, coffee, sugar . . . Most of us will spend the next few days trying to find ways of slipping these goodies to our Polish hosts without giving offence.

At Warsaw airport we are met by members of the English Institute of the University, and the English Language Officer of the British Council. First impressions are of a country that seems surprisingly, almost disappointingly normal. Traffic on the road from the airport to the city is heavy. What looks like a line of parked cars at the kerbside, however, turns out to be a mile-long queue for petrol. Many of the cars are unoccupied: their owners leave them, sometimes overnight, to reserve a place in the queue. Queues and shortages are the main features of the current Polish scene to be reported in the West, and we stare out of the windows of the British Council minibus with almost ghoulish eagerness to have our expectations confirmed. There are indeed queues to be seen in downtown Warsaw, but one's apocalyptic visions of an entire nation standing perpetually in line for the necessities of life prove to be exaggerated. This is not to underestimate the gravity of the crisis, but, so far at least, it seems to amount to acute inconvenience rather than real suffering. When you ask people to describe their present mood, the mood of the nation, the most common answer is "We are very tired."

After registering at the University, we are taken by bus and car to Jablonna, a small palace built, in neoclassical style, on the outskirts of Warsaw in the late eighteenth century. Like almost every building of consequence in the city, it was destroyed in World War II, and carefully restored. It is now a conference centre belonging to the Polish Academy of Sciences, and is to be our home for the next three days. We are immediately apprised of the austerities of Polish life, though for reasons not directly related to the crisis: the previous day a freak storm brought down some power lines in the district, and although the palace is dimly lit from its own generators, there is no water since water is pumped electrically. We make up for the lack of hot baths at the end of our journey with nips of duty-free liquor and rueful jokes. "I have plenty of soap, but the British Council didn't tell us to bring water," I remark to the lady from Poznan. "Ah, Poland will always surprise you," she replies with a smile. "By the way," I say, "would you like some soap?" The moment seems opportune, though the offer, when I hear myself saying it, lacks finesse. She accepts with charming good humour. "I promise you it will be the last bar of soap I shall use."

At dinner in the handsome banqueting-room, with its murals, mirrors and dimly-glowing chandeliers, there are speeches of welcome. The Rector of the University congratulates the British visitors on their "courage" in making the journey to Poland at the present time. I can't honestly say I feel I deserve this accolade, nor, I think, do my colleagues: perhaps, it occurs to me, we should be more nervous than we are. Perhaps we are suffering from the blithe foolhardiness of those who have never experienced foreign occupation or seen unarmed demonstrators shot on the streets. The history of Poland over the past two centuries must be one of the most tragic among European nation-states: a long succession of defeats, occupations, betrayals, and brave but futile or mistimed uprisings. This bitter historical heritage underlies everything the Poles say and do today. It explains the intensity of their patriotism, their courage and their exhilaration at the success of Solidarity: it also explains a degree of self-obsession, a streak of fatalism, which seems stranger and more disturbing "under Western eyes" – to turn Conrad's phrase upon his native country.

Outside the formal sessions of the conference, in which we discuss somewhat haphazardly the "Quest for Identity" in nineteenth- and twentieth-century literature, the Poles talk of little except the crisis. We pump them with questions which they are only too glad to answer and debate among themselves; they seldom ask us questions in return, except: "What do they think of the Polish situation in England?" Some days later, at a party in Lodz, I asked the company what they thought about the question of Northern Ireland (the only part of the British Isles, it seemed to me, where life was remotely comparable to life in Poland) and received rather vague and underinformed answers. Obviously they had not given much thought to the matter. Likewise, the recent wave of anti-nuclear demonstrations in Western Europe touches no chord of response in the breasts of Poles. This is partly because they feel that whatever force in the world inhibits Soviet imperialism must be good for Poland; and partly because their recent history has been so terrible that the prospects of nuclear war hardly hold any terror for the Poles. This latter sentiment, though understandable, is of course quite irrational, and rather alarming, since it implies a readiness to plunge the whole world into a nuclear holocaust for the sake of Poland. The first of these considerations, however, is much more logical. When you reflect upon the matter in a Polish context it seems glaringly obvious that for the West unilaterally to renounce the possession of nuclear weapons would entail at best abandoning the peoples of Eastern Europe to indefinite servitude, and at worst inviting the same servitude for ourselves. It can be argued that this would still be preferable to the risk of nuclear war, or to the moral iniquity of threatening to use nuclear weapons: but one can't help wondering whether those who adopt this position have really imagined the price they are theoretically prepared to pay, or would maintain the position for very long if they lived in an East European country.

This is my own first visit to Eastern Europe, apart from an afternoon in East Berlin, and although Poland, I am told, has been in the last decade the most liberal of all the Warsaw Pact states, and at present enjoys unprecedented freedom of speech and action, it is still something of a shock to realize, not merely abstractly, but as it were on one's pulses, that virtually the whole of the Polish nation stands in relation to its rulers rather (to compare great things with little) as do the private soldiers in a conscript army to their regular officers, or the pupils at some repressive and corrupt boarding-school to their masters. The Poles, quite simply, did not choose the political system under which they live, and given the chance would repudiate it in favour of some kind of social democratic state with a mixed economy. This, in spite of decades of Party propaganda to the contrary. The Poles have seen the Communist future and as far as they are concerned it does not work. For the Westerner, in consequence, Poland is a looking-glass world in which many of the "progressive" and "conservative" positions in our own ideological discourse – on the economy, on disarmament, on religion, on Vietnam, even on the Boy Scouts – are queerly inverted.

After the conference disperses, I go into Warsaw to keep a lunch appointment with two people at the Catholic publishing-house Pax, which published my first novel, *The Picturegoers*, many years ago. They have been considering my last novel [*How Far Can You Go?*] but gently intimate that they have decided against it, a decision which does not surprise me. A Polish lady at the conference who had been reading it warned me that, much as she was enjoying it, it would be impossible to publish anything in Poland, at the present time, which adopted a critical or satirical stance towards Catholicism. The Church has been the main focus of spiritual and ideological resistance to Soviet Communism in Poland in the post-war years, and has played a crucial role, at once steadying and inspiring, in the events of the last year and a half. Who can forget those press and TV pictures of the striking workers in the Gdansk shipyards hearing mass in their thousands, and even going to confession in public? In such an atmosphere, it would clearly be unthinkable to criticize the Church, or to expose its internal tensions and contradictions, even in the modes of comedy and irony.

For of course there *are* tensions and contradictions. I am reliably informed, for instance, that practising Polish Catholics resort to abortion as a means of birth-control on a large scale. The state, though officially in favour of contraception, does not ensure the availability of contraceptives – the pill is particularly difficult to obtain – but does provide abortion on demand. It is possible that this state of affairs has been deliberately contrived to weaken religious allegiance. If so, it has not been very successful: but the fact remains that many Polish women, especially the unmarried (since the one-parent family is not a viable social option in Poland) see no alternative to committing what their Church teaches is a very grave sin. Thus, whereas British Catholics active in the anti-abortion campaign see themselves as trying to persuade secular society to renounce abortion, in Poland it is a moral issue for Catholics themselves. In this perspective the present Pope's teaching on sex and marriage, which to liberal Catholic opinion in the West sometimes seems not merely conservative but decidedly eccentric, becomes much more explicable, if no more universally relevant.

My publishers hand over to me some zlotys, royalties on *The Picturegoers (Kinomani)* which have been blocked here since its publication in 1966. They are now worth about £280 at the official rate of exchange, a tenth of that at the "real" (i.e. black-market) rate. The pursuit of hard currency in Warsaw seems to have reached panic intensity. There is a joke in circulation giving three reasons why Poland and the United States are one and the same country: (1.) In America you can criticize President Reagan, and in Poland you can criticize President Reagan. (2.) In America you can buy anything for dollars and in Poland you can buy anything for dollars. (3.) In America you can buy nothing for zlotys and in Poland you can buy nothing for zlotys.

By the afternoon of Friday it is apparent to me that I have caught a bad cold, which not only limits my energy for sightseeing, but perhaps casts a certain gloom of spirit over the little I do undertake. The streets and squares of Warsaw seem drab, chilly and inhospitable under lowering grey cloud. The meticulously restored Old Town has already weathered sufficiently to look quite convincingly old, but it seems to me somehow lifeless. Mainly, I think, it is the lack of colours, of signs, lights, advertisements such as one is accustomed to in Western cities, that creates this depressing effect. Beyond the precincts of the Old Town, the skyline is dominated by the Palace of Culture, an immense edifice in the Soviet skyscraper-wedding-cake style of architecture that towers hundreds of feet above any other building, like one of the Ministries in *1984*. It was a gift from the Russian people, and is easily the most hated building in the whole of Poland.

On Sunday I attend mass at the academic church just outside the perimeter of the Old Town, a baroque building full of saints and angels in billowing gold leaf – all restored, presumably, since there was a battle in the church during the war, between Poles and Germans. The congregation, filling the church to overflowing, is predominantly young, sober, attentive and earnest. Unfortunately the sermon, and the bidding prayers, both entirely unintelligible to me, are so extended that I am obliged to leave before the mass is over in order to meet the British Council driver who is to take me to Lodz, where I am to lecture as guest of the University. Lodz is pronounced "Woodge", that much I have learned; but I am a poor linguist at the best of times, and Polish has reduced me to linguistic near-impotence. It is a great embarrassment to me that I cannot even remember the names of people I am introduced to, since my usual mnemonic systems simply don't apply.

The British Council driver does not speak English, and I am nursing a sore throat anyway, so we pass the two-hour journey in silence broken only by the slurping of the emergency petrol can in the back of the Cortina Estate – an exotic vehicle amid all the endless Ladas and Fiats (built in Poland under licence). The traffic thins as soon as we pass the outskirts of Warsaw. We drive through flat, sodden country over which the hand of winter seems raised threateningly, ready to fall with snow and ice. There is scarcely a leaf to be seen. Peasant women walking home from mass with bright shawls thrown over their heads and shoulders, and wayside shrines like gaudily painted telephone boxes, with saints and madonnas ensconced behind glass, afford the only flashes of colour in the passing scene. The small towns we pass through seem desolate places: muddy, unmade-up verges to the roads, peeling paint, crumbling façades, disconsolate groups of people waiting for buses, stepping out into the road in a desperate attempt to hitch a ride.

Lodz is a large industrial town based on textiles, sometimes described as the Polish Manchester. I was prepared for something rather grim, but the centre of the city in fact makes a not unattractive impression, laid out in a grid of broad streets and boulevards lined with fine houses that have interestingly decorated façades, a little reminiscent of Vienna. Unlike most Polish cities, Lodz was scarcely damaged in World War II, though it has its dark wartime history: thirty per cent of the pre-war population was Jewish, and very few of them survived. The wealthiest Jewish family bought themselves a safe passage to Switzerland: their palatial town residence now accommodates the municipal museum. Their less fortunate brethren were herded together in the ghetto with Jews brought in from outlying districts, en route to Auschwitz and other extermination camps. It seems incredible that anti-semitism could survive in a country in which the camps are preserved as monuments, yet there was an ugly outbreak of it in the late 60s, and even now, I am told, some who disapprove of Solidarity are apt to suggest that there is too strong a Jewish element in its leadership. Would a Polish Faulkner make anti-semitism the nation's Second Fall, like slavery in the Southern States?

I am booked into the Hotel Swiatowit, an imposing modern building at first sight, though on closer acquaintance somewhat shoddy in detail. It is certainly a less interesting place than the pre-war Europejski in Warsaw, with its shabby splendours of mirror and marble, hard-currency whores discreetly plying their trade amid the potted palms. But in Lodz I am invited into Polish homes for the first time, and able to get a little closer to the realities of Polish life. My escort and guide, E., a young teaching assistant working toward her PhD in phonology, takes me, as soon as I arrive, to have a late lunch with Dr M., a single, middle-aged lady who is a lecturer in the Department of English. She lives in a tiny apartment, in a rather neglected-looking block, such as an old-age pensioner with no independent means might occupy in Britain. She serves a pleasant meal of mushroom soup, breaded veal cutlets, cake and tea, which I consume gratefully though guiltily, thinking of the queueing and coupons it must have cost.

Dr M. is a fervent Catholic and patriot – to her the two things go together, and she seems slightly disconcerted to learn that I am a Catholic too, almost as if she thought Catholicism were the special property of the Poles. The pontificate of Pope John Paul II has rather encouraged this proprietorial attitude. It is certainly impossible to exaggerate the contribution of the Pope, and especially of his triumphal return to Poland after his election, to the resurgence of national spirit and the success of Solidarity. It is, for the same reason, impossible to criticize the Pope in Poland, or even to suggest that he is a conservative in theological and pastoral matters. Dr M. remarks that Hans Küng's description of the Polish Church as authoritarian was "insulting". She speaks slowly, precisely, formally. Our talk is polite but serious, with none of the jokes, evasions and polite qualifications that would characterize such a conversation between strangers in England. We discuss the crisis, the films of Wajda, Polish history, Catholicism, the Pope. I introduce the subject of nuclear disarmament. "Of course," she says, "unilateral disarmament means death." She smiles the sort of smile with which one tries to take the offence from stating a childishly obvious truth. She concedes the difficulty of reconciling the use of nuclear weapons with Christian principles, but this is obviously a vaguer, more problematic issue to her than the other side of the equation. A young woman at the end of World War II, she seems to look back upon the Stalinist period that immediately followed with even greater horror than the German occupation, perhaps because it was a time of *trahison des clercs*, when the universities, especially in the humanities, were deeply compromised by ideological indoctrination. Even E., who grew up in the period of the Thaw, can remember the humiliation of having to parrot the party line when addressing a group of Girl Scouts under the surveillance of a party officer. There must be few adult educated Poles who do not have the memory of some such episode in the past – hence the exhilaration with which they now observe the authority and membership of the Party crumbling away.

E. is a composed, friendly but unflirtatious girl who spent two years at Atlantic College in Wales in her late teens, an experience which helped her achieve her perfect command of English, but also in a way permanently unfitted her for the life she can expect in Poland. She finds Lodz a boring city, and would like to be more independent, but there are insuperable obstacles, both social and economic, to her moving away, or even out of the parental home. This, of course, mainly because she is a girl. Poland is deeply traditionalist in its attitudes to women and their social roles. Althought most women work and many achieve high standing in certain professions (e.g. the teaching of English literature in universities), they are expected to fulfil the traditional duties of the wife and mother at the same time. There are few women among the leaders of Solidarity.

I return to Warsaw in an overheated train, and check into the Europejski for one night – my last. Two experiences in the course of the evening epitomize the two moods of contemporary Poland – one buoyant and hopeful, the other anxious and pessimistic. The chambermaid who brings mineral water to my room is a thin, frail-looking middle-aged woman, with a gentle, lined face. She speaks a little English, and quickly establishes that I am from England, a university professor, about to return home. "What do you think of Poland?" she asks. "Very nice," I reply politely; then, as her face creases with incredulity, I add: "Nice people." "Nice people," she agrees wryly. "But things are terrible here. We have nothing. Nothing." She looks at me more with curiosity than with envy, as if trying to imagine what it must be like to be a prosperous Englishman, about to return to a land of plenty. "You would not change a pound, half a pound?" she asks tentatively – then anticipates my reply: "No, you do not need, tomorrow you go to England." I give her my last bar of soap, for which she thanks me effusively: it is one person's ration for two months. "You are very lucky," she says, "to be English." I don't feel inclined to disagree.

It is 11 November, Polish Independence Day, since the modern state came into being after the Great War. The date has been only perfunctorily honoured by the Communist regime, which prefers to stress the "liberation" of 1945. But this evening Solidarity has organized – perhaps "improvised" would be the more accurate term – a huge procession from the Cathedral of St John in the Old Town to the tomb of the Unknown Soldier, which faces the Europejski across a vast, barren square. Just after seven, X., a young lecturer at Warsaw University, calls at the hotel with a package for me to mail in England, and we go out into the streets to observe the demonstration, for that is what it is. Large crowds, summoned mainly by word of mouth, have turned out on this frosty evening to line the pavements and applaud the marchers – unions, Boy Scouts, and many other groups, some of them illegal, like the movement for an independent Poland. One banner says simply: "Katyn

1940", a reference to the massacre of Polish officers which, according to the official account, was carried out in 1941 by the Germans, but which most Poles believe was perpetrated by the Russians a year earlier. The marchers sing songs from the First World War which have not been heard in public for many years. X. and I go back to my hotel room, which overlooks the square and the floodlit tomb of the Unknown Soldier. X. telephones his wife and, standing at the open window, through which the amplified speeches carry to us, describes the scene to her, like a war correspondent. "She says there is nothing about it on the radio," he says to me. His eyes are bright with excitement. "If you had told me a year ago that such a demonstration could take place in the streets of Warsaw I would not have believed you." Since X. is younger, and stronger, than the chambermaid, one may hope that he, rather than she, represents Poland's future.

Shakin' Stevens Superstar (1982)

Shakin' Stevens is an amiable and athletic young Welshman who sings rock and roll songs roughly in the style of Elvis Presley. He has sold, at the last count, about seven million LP albums and about ten million singles all around the world. He was recently voted Top Male Vocalist in the British Pop and Rock Awards. He is at present in the middle of a nationwide tour which began with a concert at the Odeon, Birmingham, where I accompanied a party of young teenagers.

At a pop concert, as distinct from a rock, folk or jazz concert, the primary motive of those who attend would appear to be the adoration of the star. It is a quasi-religious occasion, in which spectacle is quite as important as the music, and the worshippers are predominantly pubescent or pre-pubescent girls.

It is often said that rock and roll is essentially Dionysian in spirit. The blatantly sexual hip movements of Presley and his imitators, and the collective hysteria of their fans, certainly encourage such interpretation. But watching Shakin' Stevens, I was more struck by the Christian symbolism permeating the entire event.

All pop concerts begin with a support group. Its function is that of John the Baptist: to herald the star. They must be musically compatible with, but inferior to him. They perform on a bare desert of a stage under stark lights, in front of the curtain behind which an elaborate set is being prepared for the star. The support group for Shakin' Stevens is called The Stargazers, which perhaps suggests the Magi. They are a kind of parody of Bill Haley and the Comets (so were Bill Haley and the Comets, as Oscar Wilde might have said). "Shakin' Stevens is coming soon," their lead singer promised a restive audience, and was rewarded with an anticipatory scream – a mere whisper to what was to come.

After an extremely long interval, raising the audience's expectations to fever pitch, the curtain rises on a dimly-lit stage, divided by three sloping ramps, between which the nine-piece band is distributed. The star's first appearance has Old Testament overtones: a shadowy figure stalks down the central ramp, to the accompaniment of portentous chords and drumbeats, and amid flashes and explosions and clouds of smoke. But then the lights come on, flickering in rainbow colours to the beat of the music, and Shakin' Stevens – "Shaky", as he is affectionately known – comes to the front of the stage, smiling, youthful, friendly, to receive a delirious welcome. The Father transformed into the Son.

The performance itself combines features of both Ministry and Passion. At frequent intervals young girls, watchfully observed by uniformed security guards, step to the front of the auditorium and, stretching up to the stage, beseech their idol to accept bouquets, teddy bears, knickers and paper hearts. By the end of the show, the front of the stage is littered with these votive offerings. Some girls proffer handkerchiefs and scarves with which the star dabs the sweat from his brow before handing them back to these diminutive Veronicas, who return raptly to their seats, clutching the precious relics. A more mature young woman in a red dress manages to get up on to the stage and throws herself enthusiastically upon Shaky, but this Mary Magdalen is quickly collared by the uniformed disciples and hustled away.

Then, as the show approaches its climax, as if in obedience to some intuitive, collective impulse, the fans in the front stalls surge forward, overwhelming the security guards, and stand in a heaving, swaying crowd, pressed up against the edge of the stage, arms raised in worship, fingers splayed imploringly. Two tiny tots are allowed up on to the stage and Shaky crouches to let them sing with him into the mike. ("Suffer little children . . .")

The star jerks and gyrates in ever more energetic and exhausting spasms. He turns cartwheels and on occasion throws himself tragically to the ground. ("And he fell for the first time . . .") Eventually he sings his last number and bids his worshippers goodbye.

The encore is, of course, a well-established convention of concerts, planned and rehearsed before the performance begins, but seldom, I imagine, has it been attended with such religious solemnity as in this case. The stage is left dark and silent for a daringly long time. The audience's applause after the star's exit dies away and they begin to chant and wail, "We want Shaky! We want Shaky!" Then, at last, faint music is audible, plangent guitar chords and muffled drumbeats. Something strange and supernatural is happening on stage. The central ramp is rising in the air, like the jaws of hell opening, and brilliant beams of light suddenly shine out, dazzling the audience. Out of the darkness and the dazzle comes . . . Shaky! He is risen! Crashing chords, flashing lights, delirious rejoicing – and three encores.

After the Resurrection comes the Ascension. The ramp is lowered again and Shaky slowly climbs it to a platform at the back of the stage, where the backdrop suddenly acquires a mirrored surface, reflecting back to the audience their own image, but at a higher level, so that it seems as if Shaky is returning to a heavenly host, their arms raised in hallelujahs.

At last he is really, finally gone. But in the foyer on the way out you can buy a long white scarf with his image imprinted on it.

My Joyce (1982)

This is not, as the title may suggest, a memoir of my personal acquaintance with James Joyce. Our paths never crossed, which is hardly surprising, given that I was not yet six years of age, and had never been out of England, when he died in Zurich, on 13 January 1941, at the end of his long Continental exile. No, this is a rather personal essay on his literary influence, and perhaps "the anxiety of influence" – though, for reasons to be suggested later, that seems a somewhat pretentious claim. I studied Joyce at school and college; I teach Joyce now, myself, to students at the University of Birmingham; and I have written academic literary criticism about his work. But I also write novels – have done so since the age of seventeen – and my reading of Joyce has inevitably shaped and affected that enterprise. I say "inevitably" because we know that books are made out of other books as much as they are made out of their authors' personal experience, and it would be impossible for a contemporary novelist with any kind of artistic ambition, however modest, not to have felt, if only indirectly, the influence of the greatest innovator in modern prose fiction. There is a kind of influence that modern criticism calls "intertextuality", and it is inescapable.

In my own case, however, there were personal, socio-cultural reasons why I not only read Joyce, but was in a sense "written" by him too, in the crucially formative years of adolescence and early adulthood. Because my mother was a Roman Catholic (her father was a Cork man called Murphy who ran a series of pubs in South East London) and my father a tolerant non-denominational Christian, I had a Catholic upbringing and education. Due to the disturbances of war, I attended a good many primary schools in different parts of England, but most of them were Catholic parochial schools or private schools run by nuns. Back in London after the war, I received my secondary schooling at a local Catholic "grammar school" run by the De la Salle Brothers. My adolescent social life revolved around the parish soccer team and the parish youth club. Thus I grew up within the intangible, but very real, walls of the Catholic "ghetto". I inhabited a world ideologically shaped and interpreted by Counter-Reformation Catholicism – which was not very different in England in the late 1940s from the Catholicism in which James Joyce grew up: the liturgy and its language were the same, the theology was the same, the manners and morals were very similar. English Catholics were mostly Irish or partly Irish in origin, in the lower-middle-class social stratum to which I belonged, and many of the priests and teachers I encountered spoke with a thick brogue. Thus to read *A Portrait of the Artist as a Young Man*, as I did at the age of sixteen, at the suggestion of my English teacher (an Irish layman), was to experience immediate recognition. How well, for instance, I recognized the anger of Stephen's Jesuit teachers, the special anger of priests and religious that is the sour byproduct of consecrated repression, of vowed poverty, chastity and obedience; an anger that seems, to the children who are so often its victims, puzzlingly excessive and difficult to reconcile with the idea of holiness.

Stephen, glancing timidly at Father Arnall's dark face, saw that it was a little red from the wax that he was in.

Was that a sin for Father Arnall to be in a wax or was he allowed to get in a wax when the boys were idle because that made them study better or was he only letting on to be in a wax? It was because he was allowed because a priest would know what a sin was and would not do it. But if he did it one time by mistake what would he do to go to confession?

Sin. Confession. These loomed very large in the consciousness of practising Catholics in the days before Vatican II. It was a narrowly, obsessively eschatological faith.

The name of the game was Salvation, the object to get to Heaven and avoid Hell. It was like Snakes and Ladders: sin sent you plummeting down towards the Pit; the sacraments, good deeds, acts of self-mortification, enabled you to climb back towards the light. Everything you did or thought was subject to spiritual accounting . . .

Thus begins a passage in a recent novel of mine, *How Far Can You Go?* (1980). It uses an authorial mode of address in order to foreground the quaint obsolescence of the system of belief described – and also to convey basic information about Catholicism to a largely secular audience. Joyce, of course, eschewed such a method. He cultivated authorial impersonality and invisibility, focalized the narrative of *A Portrait* exclusively through Stephen, and made no concessions to the non-Catholic (or non-Irish) reader by way of authorial glossing. Nevertheless, the irony in my passage perhaps owes something to the more subtle and interiorized irony of the opening of the fourth section of *A Portrait*, describing the period of piety in Stephen's adolescence, following the traumatic "retreat" at his school:

> His daily life was laid out in devotional areas. By means of ejaculations and prayers he stored up ungrudgingly for the souls in purgatory centuries of days and quarantines and years; yet the spiritual triumph which he felt in achieving with ease so many fabulous ages of canonical penances did not wholly reward his zeal of prayer since he could never know how much temporal punishment he had remitted by way of suffrage for the agonizing souls; and, fearful lest in the midst of the purgatorial fire, which differed from the infernal only in that it was not everlasting, his penance might avail no more than a drop of moisture, he drove his soul daily through an inceasing circle of works of supererogation.
>
> Every part of his day, divided by what he regarded now as the duties of his station in life, circled about its own centre of spiritual energy. His life seemed to have drawn near to eternity; every thought, word, and deed, every instance of consciousness could be made to revibrate radiantly in heaven: and at times his sense of such immediate repercussion was so lively that he seemed to feel his soul in devotion pressing like fingers the keyboard of a great cash register and to see the amount of his purchases start forth immediately in heaven, not as a number, but as a frail column of incense or as a slender flower.

In one vital respect my own situation as a young Catholic was very different from that of Joyce/Stephen. In the section of Irish society to which he belonged, the Church exerted a very powerful influence of repression and control not only over faith and morals, but over culture too. Hence it was inevitable that in seeking to fulfil his artistic vocation Joyce (and Stephen) should rebel against the Church. Yet the only alternative ideological spaces available in Ireland itself were those of the Protestant Ascendancy – the instrument of colonialist repression and exploitation – or the "cultic twalette" of the Irish Literary Renaissance for which Joyce had little sympathy or intellectual respect. Hence, in rebelling against his own Irish Catholic middle-class culture, Joyce necessarily committed himself to exile, to flight to some neutral ground. "When the soul of a man is born in this country," Stephen tells Davin, "there are nets flung at it to hold it back from flight. You talk to me of nationality, language, religion. I shall try to fly by those nets."

My own situation was very different. No great courage or determination was needed by an English Catholic to leave the Church in the 1940s or early 50s: you simply walked out into the predominantly secular, liberal, post-Christian society that stretched beyond the walls of the ghetto. Thousands of young people "lapsed" every year. In some ways the more interesting, challenging thing to do was to stay inside the ghetto – or, rather, to pass through its gates without renouncing its fundamental beliefs and values. To Joyce, in his Irish context at the turn of the century, the Catholic Church was a force antipathetic and inimical to the exercise of the literary imagination: distrustful of independent thought, suspicious of novelty, indifferent to beauty and fearful of sexuality. This was also true of the Catholicism I experienced in school and parish – but that Church had no power to impose its canons on the production and consumption of art, since its authority covered only a minority, and a socially and educationally depressed minority, within British society as a whole. Furthermore, there had evolved, mostly after Joyce's formative years, a tradition of Catholic literature and thought, mainly constituted by converts, such as Newman, Hopkins, Chesterton, Waugh and Greene, and fed from Continental sources such as Huysmans, Bloy, Péguy, Bernanos and Mauriac, which made Catholic belief seem a potential asset rather than an encumbrance to the aspirant writer, its uncompromising supernaturalism an invigorating challenge to the liberal, secular, materialistic values of modern Western society, in which most of its more thoughtful members seemed deeply disillusioned.

In short, I did not feel it was necessary to stop practising the Catholic faith in order to assert the spiritual independence of the artist as a young man. Like Joyce, I left school to attend my local university; but whereas Joyce's University College Dublin was controlled by the Jesuits, the same clerical order that had dominated his childhood, University College London was a wholly secular and pluralistic institution – was, indeed, the original "godless university", founded by Jeremy Bentham, whose wizened, mummified corpse is seated in a glass case under the College dome, as if in mocking commentary on the Christian doctrine of the resurrection of the body. I was glad to shake off the repressive and philistine culture of school and parish, but to identify oneself as a Catholic at University College London was to strike a rather interesting, almost exotic pose before one's peers.

What I am trying to explain is how it was that, while remaining myself a committed Catholic in my student years and after, I never hesitated in my total admiration for and devotion to Joyce, the arch-apostate from Catholicism in modern letters. The paradox is fleetingly reflected in my first novel, *The Picturegoers* (1960), an immature work, mostly written some years before it was published, which I cannot read now without embarrassment. There are several strands to the narrative, but the principal one concerns the conversion to Catholicism of a young student of secular, materialistic upbringing, as a result of lodging with a Catholic family, after having awakened in the eldest daughter desires that, wishing to try his vocation as a priest, he can no longer satisfy. It's a plot that seems superficially alien to Joyce's early work, yet the text contains a fleeting tribute to him of the kind that first novelists often like to leave as traces of their literary allegiances. A younger daughter of the family is going through a phase of adolescent rebelliousness, and the hero prescribes *A Portrait* as therapy.

> And she had read it through, soaking up like a dry sponge its sadness and revolt and rebellion and need to be free, and how she wished she could have met Stephen when he was her age, and talked to him and said how she understood.

Joyce/Stephen was an apostate, but, as Cranly pointed out to the fictional persona, remained "supersaturated with the religion in which you say you disbelieve". It was not surprising to me to learn – from, I think, William York Tindall – that one American reader actually claimed to have been converted to Catholicism through reading Joyce's books, so accurately, tangibly, *fairly*, did he represent the Faith in them. In many ways Joyce was (and is) the most Catholic of all the novelists in the English language; and it was certainly an enormous advantage to be oneself a Catholic when studying his work.

The English Honours syllabus at University College London in the early 1950s was very traditionalist, with heavy doses of compulsory Old and Middle English, and we were not allowed to expose ourselves to modern literature until the third year, when there was an optional course. The set authors for special study were Henry James and W. B. Yeats, but it was necessary to prepare oneself to answer on others in the examination, and in the second term of my final undergraduate year, 1955, I decided to embark on a reading of *Ulysses*, of which I had hitherto read only the "Hades" episode in T. S. Eliot's little selection, *An Introduction to James Joyce*. I well remember the purchase of my copy of *Ulysses*, a solemn deed not, for several reasons, to be performed lightly. The only edition available was the hardback reprint of the 1937 Bodley Head edition. It cost exactly one pound, a not inconsiderable investment for a student whose annual maintenance grant was about £150; and it was not all that readily available. It is hard to recall, now, those days of literary scarcity before the book trade succumbed to paperbacks and permissiveness. *Ulysses* was still, in 1955, the only work of imaginative literature on open sale in the United Kingdom that printed the well-known four-letter taboo words in full, and that described "perverse" sexual acts in explicit detail. Public libraries, if they possessed copies at all, kept them locked up and restricted to borrowers with *bona fide* scholarly motives, and many respectable bookshops would not stock *Ulysses*. I bought my copy, after drawing several blanks and disapproving looks, from a bookshop in Charing Cross Road, the kind that featured in its windows books of nude photographic studies and allegedly learned tomes on sexual customs and deviations.

These days I read *Ulysses* in the Penguin edition because that is what my students use, but I still have the Bodley Head edition, protected by a tattered and faded green dust jacket, bearing a generous tribute by (perhaps surprisingly) J. B. Priestley:

> As a literary feat, an example of virtuosity in narration and language, it is an astounding creation. Nobody who knows anything about writing can read the book and deny its author, not merely talent, but sheer genius.

Just to handle the old Bodley Head edition was to feel a shiver of premonitory pleasure, a sense that this was no ordinary novel, but a magic book. It was heavy, and an unusual shape, squarer than the normal novel, with long lines of type stretching from margin to margin that imposed an appropriately deliberate pace upon the reader. The reset Bodley Head edition of 1960 is no doubt a more accurate and convenient text, but it is a less talismanic object.

It was a good moment for me to discover *Ulysses* – the time when a student's reading is apt to be robbed of pleasure and his responses dulled by the encroaching shadow of final examinations. While most of my contemporaries were beginning to think of "revision", turning over stale notes in a frantic effort to revive fading memories of books already read, I was rapt in a wholly new dimension of literary experience. Since I knew I would not have time to read *Ulysses* twice before Finals, it was imperative that I should understand it as fully as possible on first reading. I therefore provided myself with Stuart Gilbert's invaluable guide, *James Joyce's "Ulysses"*, and read its chapters *pari passu* with the episodes of *Ulysses*. This procedure, which would diminish, or at least distort, the experience of reading most other novels, seemed only to enhance my enjoyment of Joyce's book. One of the remarkable features of *Ulysses*, it has always seemed to me, is the way its "sense of felt life" (Henry James's phrase) is not undermined, but rather complemented, by the elaborate patterning, allusiveness, and stylistic virtuosity of which Gilbert gave the first comprehensive account.

Like, I suppose, most first-time readers of *Ulysses* I was chiefly impressed by its sheer mimetic power, the feeling that never before had the whole range of sensory experience, from the most sublime to the most basic – from listening to music to passing a bowel movement – been so vividly, exactly, memorably captured in words; and that never before had the twists and turns and gaps and leaps in the processes of human thought been so fully understood and accurately represented. At about this time in England, the popular and sensationalist Sunday newspaper, *News of the World*, was running an advertising campaign with the slogan, "All Human Life Is Here". It seemed to me that Joyce had been robbed. All human life was in *Ulysses* – and a good deal of human history, art, learning, literature, and scientific knowledge, too. To read it carefully and attentively was a liberal education in itself. (Of course Joyce had not really been robbed – the *News of the World* had been "robbed", without knowing it, by Joyce: there was no trick of journalistic rhetoric, no inflated and grandiloquent journalistic pretension, that hadn't been already taken care of in "Aeolus".)

Reading *Ulysses* was, then, a happy culmination of my undergraduate literary studies (the "Oxen of the Sun" was like a hilarious speeded-up revision of the entire syllabus). But what was its effect on an aspirant novelist? The 1950s was a decade dominated, as far as British writing was concerned, by the "Movement" of Larkin, Amis, Wain, Davie, Enright and others; by the figure of the Angry Young Man especially associated with John Osborne's Jimmy Porter, John Braine's Joe Lampton, and the class-conscious antiheroes of Amis and Wain; by the sociologically observant fiction of Angus Wilson, C. P. Snow, William Cooper and Colin MacInnes. The fashionable *écriture*, in other words, was neorealist and anti-modernist – not a climate in which Joyce's influence was likely to be encouraged or acknowledged. Kingsley Amis adopted a symptomatic stance towards the "revolution of the word" in the course of a review written in 1958:

> The idea about experiment being the life-blood of the English novel dies hard. "Experiment", in this context, boils down pretty regularly to "obtruded oddity" whether in construction – multiple viewpoints and such – or in style; it is not felt that adventurousness in subject matter or attitude or tone really counts. Shift from one scene to the next in mid-sentence, cut down on verbs or definite articles, and you are putting yourself right up in the forefront, at any rate in the eyes of those who were reared on Joyce and Virginia Woolf and take a jaundiced view of more recent developments.

Among those developments was, of course, Amis's *Lucky Jim* (1954), a book of great verbal dexterity disguising itself as clumsiness, but rooted in an English tradition of comedy of manners quite foreign to Joyce. *Lucky Jim* was another magic book for me – and for most English readers of my age and background, upwardly mobile, scholarship-winning, first-generation university graduates – for it established precisely the linguistic register we needed to articulate our sense of social identity, a precarious balance of independence and self-doubt, irony and hope. But of course *Lucky Jim* was, by any objective critical criteria, a much slighter book than *Ulysses*, a point I worried at in one of my first published critical essays, entitled "The Modern, the Contemporary, and the Importance of Being Amis":

> I suppose that, as a Roman Catholic, I could scarcely be more distant from Amis's view of the eternal verities. And yet I constantly experience a strange community of feeling with him and find that he speaks to me in a way that the great classic novelists do not, in an idiom, a tone of voice, to which I respond with immediate understanding and pleasure, and without any conscious exertion of the kind required by critical reading . . . The question presents itself: if James's and Joyce's uses of language produce higher works of literary art than Amis's, why doesn't he follow their example? It is a good question and . . . Amis is well aware of its force. The obvious answer – "It's too difficult" – is only partly true.

Another answer, I went on to suggest, is the fact that a writer might be constrained, by the particular literary, historical, ideological moment in which he is situated, from using literary resources which he may objectively admire. I was, of course, thinking as much of myself as of Amis when I wrote this essay; for I was well aware of the gap, not to say contradiction, between my critical esteem for Joyce and the other great moderns, and my own fictional practice in *The Picturegoers* and my second novel, *Ginger, You're Barmy* (1962), both books very much in the current neorealist mode, in which the kind of spiritual and moral drama that I had encountered in Graham Greene's fiction was transposed into a homelier, more suburban key. Whatever the limitations of the "Movement" ethos – and its tendency to encourage philistinism, parochialism and chauvinism is inescapable – it opened up the literary world to young writers like myself, with no privileged, cultured background, no influential friends in the literary marketplace, no exotic or heroic experience to boast about; and I will always be grateful to it for that.

I have mentioned the work of Graham Greene, and it was on him, rather than Joyce, that my own "anxiety of influence" was focused – not surprisingly when one remembers that he was a Catholic novelist whose reputation was second to none among living writers in the 40s and 50

Kingsley Amis, who gave *The Picturegoers* a friendly review in the *Observer*, noted "two or three lapses into pea-Greene simile", and could have made more of this indebtedness. But there was also, it seems to me now, a Joycean influence on this book at a deeper structural level. The novel follows the fortunes of a number of characters whose only common link is that they attend the same cinema and/or Catholic church on the three weekends covered by the action. In the way the narrative "cuts" from one character to another as they walk about the streets of the South London suburb where the action is set, often oblivious of each other's existence, but impinging directly or indirectly on each other's lives, and in the way the narrative discourse is focalized through these characters, and their consciousness rendered in an idiom appropriate to each – in all this I now perceive the model of the "Wandering Rocks" episode of *Ulysses*.

Ginger, You're Barmy was structurally derived (as I realized many years after writing it) from Greene's *The Quiet American*, and could be linked to Joyce only in the "scrupulous meanness" (his description of the style of *Dubliners*) with which it attempted to record the life of conscript soldiers in the British Army. I had myself done National Service between undergraduate and postgraduate study, and I wrote my novel about this experience very much in the spirit of Joyce's conviction, expressed to Grant Richards about *Dubliners*, "that he is a very bold man who dares to alter in the presentment, still more to deform, whatever he has seen and heard". There is, also, in the text another fleeting, but explicit, allusion to Joyce. The agnostic narrator, in a mood of sexual frustration, confesses that, "At home that night, I sat up late reading the last chapter of *Ulysses* for the dirt, which in my morality is a kind of sin." That chapter was to play a rather more important part in my next novel, *The British Museum is Falling Down* (1965).

This was, technically, a decided change of direction in my writing. I wanted to write a comic (though not unserious) novel about the tribulations of married Catholics who tried to obey their Church's teaching on birth control. In looking about for a character, or pair of characters, and a milieu, in which to explore this theme, I turned to an idea casually jotted down in my notebook some time before, of a Catholic postgraduate student of English literature, working daily in the Reading Room of the British Museum, whose life keeps taking on the stylistic and thematic colouring of the authors he is studying. Thus came into being Adam Appleby, a young, married, impecunious Catholic graduate student, racked by the fear that his wife may be pregnant for the fourth time, who in the course of a single day is propelled through a series of picaresque adventures centring on the British Museum, each episode echoing, through parody, pastiche and allusion, the work of an established modern novelist. The shifts of style and narrative technique are naturalized by making the hero prone to daydreams, fantasies and hallucinations, which are in turn motivated by his chronic anxiety about his marital circumstances. The basic irony of Adam's plight is that the only element in his life that seems authentically his, and not already "written" by some novelist, is the very source of his anxiety. As he says, in response to the charge that he can no longer distinguish between life and literature, "Literature is mostly about having sex and not much about having children. Life is the other way round." It hardly needs to be said that this novel was for its author a means of relieving, through comedy, not only a certain amount of impatience and frustration provoked by the Catholic teaching on birth control, but also a sense of what Harold Bloom has called "belatedness" – the awareness every young writer has of the daunting weight of literary tradition, and the necessity, yet seeming impossibility, of doing something in writing that has not been done already.

Early in the composition of this novel I fixed on a title which, in the event, I was not, for copyright reasons, able to use – the fourth line of the Gershwin brothers' song, "A Foggy Day":

> A foggy day in London Town
> Had me low, had me down,
> I viewed the morning with alarm,
> The British Museum had lost its charm.

It was this lyric that had consciously suggested to me the idea of limiting the action of my novel to a single day (and a foggy one). But the precedent of *Ulysses*, too, must have influenced this decision, and also encouraged me to risk the elaborate use of parody and pastiche; though, surprisingly, I did not consciously recognize this connection until the composition of the novel was fairly advanced. I wrote the novel rapidly, with more reliance on inspiration than forward planning. For obvious aesthetic reasons I wanted the last of the parodies (which included Kafka, Lawrence, Conrad, Woolf, Henry James and Hemingway among others) to be the boldest and most recognizable of all. At the same time I was aware, as the book approached its conclusion, that Adam Appleby's marital problems needed to be seen, however briefly, from another perspective than that of his wife, Barbara, if such a belated shift of viewpoint could be contrived without clumsiness. The idea of imitating "Penelope" enabled me to solve both problems at a single stroke: my novel could end, like Joyce's, with the hero returned to his home after the day's adventures, reunited with his spouse, asleep in the marital bed, while the more wakeful wife drowsily pondered the foible of men, the paradoxes of sexuality and the history of their courtship and marriage. I had always intended that Barbara's immediate anxiety about her putative pregnancy would be removed at the end of my novel. When I recalled that Molly's period also started in the last chapter of *Ulysses*, I knew, if I had not known before, that there is such a thing as writer's luck. For Molly's keyword, *yes*, I would substitute a more tentative word, more appropriate to Barbara's character and situation:

the trees came down to the beach we sat in the shade and ate the sandwiches and drank the wine the footprints in the sand were only ours the sea was empty it was like a desert island we lay down he took me in his arms shall we come back here when we're married he said perhaps I said he held me low down tight against him we'll make love in this same spot he said my dress was so thin I could feel him hard against me perhaps we'll have children with us I said then we'll come down at night he said perhaps we won't be able to afford to come at all I said you're not very optimistic he said perhaps it's better not to be I said I'm going to be famous and earn lots of money he said perhaps you won't love me then I said I'll always love you he said I'll prove it every night he kissed my throat perhaps you think that now I said but I couldn't keep it up perhaps we will be happy I said of course we will he said we'll have a nanny to look after the children perhaps we will I said by the way how many children are we going to have as many as you like he said it'll be wonderful you'll see perhaps it will I said perhaps it will be wonderful perhaps even though it won't be like you think perhaps that won't matter perhaps.

It's a colossal liberty, of course; but I hope my chapter borrows, rather than steals from the original, and does its own thing with Joyce's technique.

My next novel, *Out of the Shelter* (1970) was about a sixteen-year-old English boy's passage from innocence to experience – from a sheltered childhood a sudden exposure, in the course of a summer holiday in 1951, to Germany, the hereditary foe, and to the affluent, hedonistic society of the American Army of Occupation for whom his sister works. It's a kind of *Bildungsroman*, with an autobiographical base, and its debt to *A Portrait* and the early stories of *Dubliners* is very evident in the way the narrative is focalized through a naive consciousness but (apart from the first few pages) articulated in a mature style. In this representative passage, particularly reminiscent of "Eveline", there is actually an echo of Joyce's olfactory evocation of dear dirty Dublin, "its odours of ashpits and old weeds and offal".

From the window of the bus the familiar streets took on a strange visual clarity and resonance of association. He felt that he was seeing them for the first time as they really were, that he was responding with all his senses to the special character of South-East London, its soiled, worn textures of brick and stone, its low, irregular outline, its odours of breweries and gas and vegetables and tanneries. He noticed how old and neglected it all was: if you raised your eyes above the modern shop-fronts you saw that they had been pasted on to buildings crumbling into decay, with cracked, grimy windows and broken-backed roofs and chipped chimney-pots. The predominant colours were black, brown and dirty cream. Guinness tints.

Out of the Shelter, however, plays much safer than *A Portrait* in both surface and deep structure. It quite lacks the bold variation of styles, the poetic rhythms and leitmotifs, the disconcerting temporal gaps, and the uncompromising allusiveness of Joyce's masterpiece. In current critical jargon, *Out of the Shelter* is a much more *lisible* text than *A Portrait*, and, I fear, does not give the reader enough to do: every transition from scene to scene is carefully signposted, every scrap of information the reader needs to orient himself is thoughtfully provided, in dialogue if not in narrative.*

In *Changing Places* (1975) I went back to comedy and a Joycean variety of styles within the text. The basic plot, concerning an exchange of academic posts between an Englishman and an American, who find themselves swapping not only jobs, but attitudes, values, tastes, speech habits and ultimately wives, was so symmetrical and predictable in its operation that some stylistic variety seemed essential to keep the reader guessing and on his toes. Thus each chapter has a distinctive formal feature which distinguishes it from the others, either in temporal organization or perspective or type of discourse (letters, quotations, film script); and this variation in the narrative technique is flaunted in a series of metafictional jokes and allusions. On the whole, from Fielding and Sterne onwards, this has been the English way with self-conscious artifice in the novel: breaking the frame of realistic illusion, disturbing the smooth surface of a homogeneous prose style with abrupt shifts of tone and register, are licensed as *comic* strategies. It is as if we dare not abandon the realistic code without assuring the reader that we are only joking. Joyce himself is playing, rather than joking, in *Ulysses* and *Finnegans Wake*.

"The positive influence of Joyce has proved wide, deep and enduring," says Robert M. Adams in *Afterjoyce* (1977). "Only one novelist of his day, Franz Kafka, has exercised influence in any way comparable with

---

* I tried to mitigate this effect somewhat in the revised edition published in 1985.

Joyce's. Lawrence, Proust, Mann, Gide, Faulkner, Hemingway, and the scattering of their lesser contemporaries, are simply not in the comparison." This is true; yet it is also paradoxically true that Joyce has no successors. There are no later books in modern literature even remotely comparable to *Ulysses* and *Finnegans Wake*. Samuel Beckett, a classic case of "the anxiety of influence", saw that there was no way of building on Joyce's work and trying to go beyond it: the only hope of competing was, starting from the same premise of art as a "closed field" (Hugh Kenner's phrase) of permutable signs, to explore its implications in the antithetical direction: the direction of negation, contradiction and silence. In Beckett, Joyce's joyfully expanding verbal universe begins to contract again; its galaxies and suns stream back to their original, dense seed of primal matter, leaving only vacant space in their wake (or Wake).

Few, if any, other modern writers – certainly not the present one – have "taken on" Joyce as Beckett has. Most of us have not dreamed of measuring up to that awe-inspiring genius, but have contented ourselves with reading and raiding his work for hints, models, blueprints and lessons. His *oeuvre* is like a vast resource centre for writers, in which one may find almost every kind of literary technique: the "mythic method", the stream of consciousness, leitmotif, the uses of parody and pastiche, high styles and low styles, riveting realism and riotous fantasy, lyric, epic and dramatic modes, old words rescued from neglect, nonce words freshminted, and a whole new language, punning and polyglot, whose expressive power we are only just beginning to appreciate. You pays your money and you takes your Joyce.

Small World: An Introduction (1984)

In the 1970s I began to travel quite a bit, on academic or cultural missions; at first within Europe, then further afield, to America and the Near East. In 1982, I went round the world in three weeks, via Hong Kong, Seoul, Tokyo, Honolulu and Los Angeles. Sometimes the occasion was a lecture tour sponsored by the British Council, more often it was a conference – an international conference on some literary subject in which I have an interest, or the conference of a foreign association of university teachers of English who desired the participation of a British scholar. It seemed a convenient and economical way to see the world: your expenses were paid, and your hosts congenial company, excellent guides and fluent English speakers. There was also, of course, the opportunity to meet and discuss with one's peers matters of common professional interest; and it always struck me how unified was the discourse of literary criticism and literary theory in the modern world. The same issues and topics – mostly, in the last decade, associated with the word "structuralism", or "post-structuralism" – were being discussed and debated in identical terms in Paris, Oslo, Ankara, Rome and New York. And often by the same people.

In the last days of 1978 I went to New York to attend the famous annual convention of the MLA, the Modern Language Association of America. Though I had heard a great deal about this event, its colossal scale and frantic pace amazed and excited me. Ten thousand academics crammed into two skyscraper hotels in mid-Manhattan, listening to lectures and participating in discussions on every conceivable literary topic from "Old English Riddles" to "Faulkner Concordances", from "Lesbian-Feminist Teaching and Learning" to "Problems of Cultural Distortion in Translating Expletives in the work of Cortázar, Sender,

Baudelaire and Flaubert". I quote from the official programme, a book as thick as the telephone directory of a small town, listing 600 different events running, 30 at a time, from 8.30 in the morning to 10.15 at night over the three days of the convention.

And that was only one, perhaps the least significant level of conference activity. It was above all a place to meet people: old friends and old enemies, people whose books you had reviewed, or who had reviewed yours, people you might hire, or who might offer you a job, or an invitation to another conference. And it was clear that other, more intimate kinds of meeting were being arranged. A British colleague was accosted in the interval between his lecture and a panel discussion of it, by an attractive woman from the audience, a total stranger, who invited him to spend the night with her. "People only come to this circus to get laid," she assured him, as he struggled politely to excuse himself. She was, of course, wrong – but not entirely wrong. It is precisely the *tension* between professional self-display and erotic opportunity, between the ambition to impress many and the desire to impress one, that, among other things, makes the conference such a fascinating human spectacle, and such rich material for fiction.

The idea of writing a novel about international conference-going didn't, however, occur to me until the following June, when I attended the 7th International James Joyce Symposium. This is a biennial event held in some city associated with Joyce, and in 1979 it was held in Zurich, where he sat out the First World War, and died in the course of the Second. I remember walking, soon after checking into my hotel, towards some conference venue, and gradually becoming aware that all the other people moving in the same direction on the broad, immaculately clean Swiss pavement, were fellow academics, specialists in James Joyce, or specialists in modern fiction with an interest in James Joyce, or specialists in something or other with an interest in a subsidized trip to Zurich. I became aware, too, as we greeted each other and squinted at each other's lapel badges, that I knew many of them, or they knew me, either from some previous conference, or through our publications. Later, in the James Joyce Pub, on Pelikanstrasse, an authentic Dublin bar dismantled, transported, and lovingly reassembled in Zurich as a memorial to the great literary exile, there were many more such meetings. It began to dawn on me that jet travel had created a new academic community, a travelling caravan of professors with international contacts, lightweight luggage and generous conference grants – a global campus to which, it seemed, I now belonged myself.

From Zurich I flew direct to Tel Aviv to take part in another conference on "Poetics of Fiction and the Theory of Narrative", where the same experience was repeated – on a smaller scale, for it was a smaller, more select conference – but in a more exotic setting, providing a more piquant mixture of intellectual endeavour and hedonistic tourism. To say that I conceived *Small World* on that double conference trip would be an overstatement, but it was a gleam in my eye when I returned, exhausted, but exhilarated, to England. Two years, and many conferences later, I began writing the novel, setting it in 1979.

For me a novel usually starts when I realize that some segment or plane of my own experience has a thematic interest and unity which might be expressed through a fictional story. Then I look for some structural idea which will release and contain that potential meaning. In the case of *Small World* I knew broadly what the novel was going to be about – the vanity of human wishes as exhibited in the jet-propelled peregrinations of scholars around the global campus, from China to Peru; and I decided, at an early stage that the characters would include the exchanging professors of my earlier novel, *Changing Places*, Philip Swallow and Morris Zapp, whose fortunes I had left conveniently indeterminate at the end of that novel, as well as a young hero and heroine who would be novices in the glamorous world of academic travel, and a host of other characters of divers nationalities.

I wanted the novel to deal in a carnival spirit with the various competing theories of literary criticism which were animating and dividing the profession of letters and with the complex relations between academic scholarship, creative writing, publishing and the media which are such a striking feature of contemporary culture. But it was some time before I found the structural principle that would enable me to put all these things together in a unified narrative.

When I think I have identified a subject for a novel, I dedicate to the project a notebook, in which I jot down ideas, character sketches, draft synopses, jokes, situations, and memos to myself. Looking through my *Small World* notebook, I find very early on the prophetic remark: "The main problem is to find some plot mechanism that will bring together a large number of varied academic types from different countries, and involve them in meeting each other frequently in different places and in different combinations, and have continuous narrative interest." It was a problem which frustrated me for a long time. Some thirty pages later in the notebook there is a somewhat desperate cry: "What could provide the basis for a *story*?" And just below that: "Could some myth serve, as in *Ulysses*?" (I was thinking of the way Joyce used the story of Odysseus to give shape to one day in the lives of several modern Dubliners.) And just below that: "E.g. the Grail legend – involves a lot of different characters and long journeys."

What made me think of the Grail legend? Well, I had just been to see the somewhat preposterous but very enjoyable film, *Excalibur*, and been reminded of what a wonderfully gripping narrative it was, the story of King Arthur and the knights of the Round Table. But I was thinking also of T. S. Eliot's use of the Grail legend in *The Waste Land* as a structural device comparable to Joyce's use of the *Odyssey* – the Grail legend as reinterpreted by Jessie Weston in her book *From Ritual to Romance*. According to Jessie Weston, the Christian and chivalric motivation of the Grail knights' quest was a displaced and sublimated version of a more ancient and pagan fertility religion, centring on the myth of an impotent king and his sterile kingdom – a thesis that lent itself to Eliot's vision of sexual and spiritual sterility in the modern world. I saw analogies with the various kinds of frustration and failure that afflict writers and critics in contemporary culture, and with the ironic tension between ambition and desire in the lives of literary intellectuals which the institution of the conference tends to dramatize. And the more I thought, and read, about *romance* as a genre, extending far beyond the medieval tales of King Arthur and his knights, from the Greek romances of antiquity, to the Renaissance epic romances of Ariosto and Spenser, and the romantic comedies and tragicomedies of Shakespeare, the more convinced I became that I had found the structural principle for *Small World*. It would be not so much an academic novel, as an academic romance – academic in the double sense of dealing with academics, but also drawing on a traditional rather than a contemporary notion of romance as a genre.

It's very easy – dangerously easy – for me to give a commentary on my own fiction. Being an academic critic myself, I have all the appropriate terms and methods of analysis at my fingertips. For the same reason, I am a very self-conscious novelist. As I write, I make the same demands upon my own text as I do, in my critical capacity, on the texts of other writers. Every part of the novel, every incident, character, word even, must make an identifiable contribution to the whole. So it would be very easy for me to explain everything in *Small World* in terms of artistic cause and effect. But to do that would be, for several reasons, counter-productive. The reasons have to do with the tricky concept of authorial intention – one of those questions that are hotly debated at academic conferences.

In a classic article called "The Intentional Fallacy", two American literary theorists called W. K. Wimsatt and Monroe C. Beardsley argued that "the design or intention of an author is neither available nor desirable as a standard for judging the success of a work of literary art". This assertion appears to fly in the face of common sense, and many literary scholars of a commonsense disposition have continued unabashed to research the lives and letters of authors for evidence of their artistic intentions. But there is considerable force in the argument of Wimsatt and Beardsley that if the writer succeeded in carrying out his intentions, the work itself is the evidence, and if he didn't succeed, or succeeded in doing something else, the intention is irrelevant.

A more recent, more radical anti-intentionalist school of criticism has rejected the whole idea of the author as sovereign source or origin of a literary text. The very word "author" has become a dirty one in these quarters, replaced by "writer", one who writes – or rather one who is written, by language itself. The writer merely brings the infinite signifying power of language into play; the production of meaning is the work of the reader. "The birth of the reader," said Roland Barthes, "must be at the cost of the death of the author."

It will be obvious from what I have said about the genesis of *Small World* that I can't go along with this radical decentring of the literary text. It simply doesn't answer to my experience of writing a novel, the hard work of imagining and describing and interweaving a network of human fortunes in time and space in a way which makes simultaneous sense on a number of different levels – generic, rhetorical, moral, psychological, social, historical, and so on. Writing, especially the writing of narrative, is a process of constant choice and decision-making: to make your hero do this rather than that, to describe the action from this angle rather than that. How can one decide such questions except in terms of some overall design – which is in some sense a design upon one's putative readers? *Small World* is a comedy as well as a romance, and comedy is perhaps the genre that offers most resistance to post-structuralist aesthetics. Things that make us laugh in books rarely happen by accident, nor are they produced by readers; they are constructed by authors.

On the other hand (there is always another hand in these matters) I would not claim that, because I could explicate my own novel line by line, that is *all* it could mean; and I am well aware of the danger of inhibiting the interpretive freedom of the reader by a premature display of my own, as it were, "authorized" interpretation. A novel is in one sense a game, a game that requires at least two players, a reader as well as a writer. The writer who seeks to control or dictate the responses of his reader outside the boundaries of the text itself is comparable to a card-player who gets up periodically from his place, goes round the table to look at his opponent's hand, and advises him what cards to play. I hope I haven't already been guilty of spoiling anyone's sport in this way.

As Frank Kermode has pointed out in his recent *Essays on Fiction*, we tend to associate value with secrecy in literary as well as religious texts. The books we esteem most highly do not yield up their meanings most readily; and modern authors – Joyce and Eliot being cases in point – have found many ingenious ways of making the task of reading rewardingly difficult. As Kermode also shows, books may have, perhaps *always* have, secrets hidden from the authors themselves, however self-conscious the latter may be. This follows, as the deconstructionists never tire of telling us, from the systematic and collective nature of language and literary convention, which have the capacity to generate meanings in excess of and even in contradiction to the individual subject who uses them. The writer can only learn these secrets from his readers. Over to you.

Why Do I Write?

At the age of fifty, and with a dozen or so books published, it does not seem tautologous to say that I write because I am a writer. To stop writing, not to write, is now unthinkable – or perhaps it is the secret fear to assuage which one goes on writing. My sense of my own identity is so intimately connected with my writing that if I ceased to write I should become, in Orwellian language, an unperson to myself.

I write many different kinds of discourse: novels, short stories, academic literary criticism, book reviews, journalism of various kinds. I have recently tried my hand at writing for the stage and screen. I get satisfaction from extending my range, learning new techniques and conventions, reaching new audiences. I take professional pride in being able to write, say, a paper for a scholarly journal, an introduction to a popular edition of a classic text, and a comic novel, all of which are equally effective in their own ways.

Writing is the only thing I am really good at, and it is too late now to become really good at anything else. I am, I think, a competent and conscientious university teacher, but I know there are others who are more dedicated and inspiring. I enjoy the non-verbal arts and various sports, but have never excelled at any of them. As one gets older the possibilities of pleasure and achievement inevitably narrow. My eyesight and hearing is deteriorating, my joints stiffen. I shall probably never learn, now, to ski or to windsurf or to play a musical instrument or to speak a foreign language fluently. But there is no reason why I should not go on writing, perhaps even improving as a writer, into old age.

My desire to be a writer goes back a long way. The first serious notion of a career that I can recall entertaining was that of journalist, when I was about ten or eleven. Since my main interest in life then was sport, I had fantasies of being a sports journalist, and conscientiously practised writing reports of the professional football matches that I attended in South East London. I always read a great deal for pleasure (was there ever a writer who did not?) mainly light, juvenile literature in those days, but occasionally classic novels and some of the English humourists for whom my father (a professional dance musician with little formal education) had a particular affection – early Dickens, Jerome K. Jerome, W. W. Jacobs. When I was about fifteen he introduced me to Evelyn Waugh, for whom I developed a precocious enthusiasm. At about the same time a new English master at my school awakened my interest in poetry and the intellectual satisfaction to be derived from analysing it. I began to feel the itch to produce on others the exciting, illuminating effect that literature had on me. I started to write poems, stories and essays, and published some in the school magazine. The needle of my ambition now pointed unwaveringly towards a career of writer-critic. This led me to read English at University College London, and eventually to a double life as university teacher and novelist.

I have never felt that my academic career, and the academic publications that forwarded it, were secondary to that of the novelist, merely a secure source of income. Over the past twenty years I have published a critical book and a novel more or less in alternation. But undoubtedly writing fiction has given me more satisfaction, and more anxiety, than writing literary criticism.

Creative or imaginative writing is usually valued above critical writing, and rightly so. It is more difficult to excel in it, it is riskier, it is more unpredictable. To write a novel is to fill a hole that nobody, including oneself, was aware of until the book came into existence. First there was nothing there; then, a year or two (or three) later, there is something – a book, a whole little world of imagined people and their interlocking fortunes. When it is finished, it seems inconceivable that it should never have existed, yet when you started it you could never have predicted how it would turn out, or even been certain that you would be able to finish it.

Of course, it is always possible to finish a novel in the purely formal sense, to bring its narrative sequence to some kind of conclusion. And always, as one writes, there is the temptation to hurry the book to its end to relieve the suspense about one's ability to finish it. One must be prepared to wait; to ponder, and re-read, and re-write what one has written, until one sees the way ahead that satisfies one's own criteria of coherence, complexity, authenticity. That is what makes writing such an exhausting and stressful process – and, when it comes out right, such an exhilarating one.

Even writing the shortest book review entails the same process of risk, uncertainty, self-testing. And there, certainly, is one reason why I write, though it is not peculiar to writing. The same motive has made other men soldiers, politicians, mountaineers and philanderers. Writing has the advantage over these other activities that its achievements are permanent. Texts are not merely remembered, they are recreated every time they are read by another. And there, I venture to say, at the risk of seeming pretentious, is the ultimate reason for writing: the chance to defy death, by leaving some trace of oneself, however slight, behind.

It is, of course, also pleasant to be recognized, and rewarded, while one is still alive.

PART II

Literary and Critical

Anglo-American Attitudes (1965):

DECORUM IN BRITISH AND AMERICAN FICTION

I cannot recall who described Britain and America as two nations divided by a common language, but the epigram indicates very concisely why the literatures of these two countries afford a uniquely rewarding opportunity for comparative study. The current orthodoxy on the differences between English and American fiction may be found in such books as Richard Chase's *The American Novel and Its Tradition*. According to Chase, the English novel is "notable for its great practical sanity, its powerful engrossing composition of wide ranges of experience into a moral centrality, and equability of judgement". It is, characteristically, realistic in its depiction of life, "middlebrow" in intellectual temper and, naturally enough in view of the society out of which it grew, preoccupied with "manners".

The American fictional imagination, on the other hand, "has been stirred . . . by the aesthetic possibilities of radical forms of alienation, contradiction and disorder". It has assimilated, precariously, to the novel form the conventions of romance, and manifests "an assumed freedom from the ordinary novelistic requirements of verisimilitude, development and continuity; a tendency towards melodrama and idyll; a more or less formal abstractness and, on the other hand, a tendency to plunge into the underside of consciousness; a willingness to abandon moral questions or to ignore the spectacle of man in society, or to consider these things only indirectly or abstractly". In brief, the American novel, though lacking the solidity, poise and completeness of the English novel, is more daring, and goes deeper into the human condition.

Another way of distinguishing between English and American fiction, which runs sometimes alongside, sometimes athwart Chase's scheme, is by reference to language, and I propose to devote my remarks to this side of the question. I believe it is widely recognized that in fiction, as in poetry, America offers more achievement and excitement today than England. And certainly one reason for this is that American writers seem to be trying to do more with their medium, which is language.

Linguistic interpretations of the American literary tradition are customarily centred on the idea of the American vernacular as a source of literary vitality. Whereas Chase's tradition begins with James Fenimore Cooper's stilted, but mythically suggestive tales of the wilderness, in the vernacular scheme the American novel comes of age with Mark Twain (notorious critic of Cooper), who in Huck Finn found a voice, non-literary yet articulate – even poetic – tough yet tender, humorous yet troubled, a voice which expressed the American experience. Ernest Hemingway formulated this reading of American fiction (in which he himself occupies a key position) when he said "all modern American literature comes from one book by Mark Twain called *Huckleberry Finn*."

Unfortunately the American vernacular has served, on occasion, as the rallying cry for a certain literary nationalism or isolationism. That is, from time to time American writers who eschewed the vernacular – like Henry James – are brought before the bar of a kind of literary Un-American Activities Committee and found guilty of treason. Such criticism is a legacy of the revolt against the Genteel Tradition at the turn of the century, and obscures the real significance of the vernacular. As Mark Twain first employed it, the vernacular *is* a vital element in American fiction. But it is not in itself enough to define the American fictional achievement; and its influence has been more than American.

Consider these three passages:

(1) You don't know about me without you have read a book by the name of *The Adventures of Tom Sawyer*, but that ain't no matter. That book was made by Mr Mark Twain and he told the truth, mainly.

(2) If you really want to know about it, the first thing you'll probably want to know is where I was born, and what my lousy childhood was like, and how my parents were occupied and all before they had me, and all that David Copperfield kind of crap, but I don't feel like going into it, if you want to know the truth.

(3) As soon as I got to Borstal they made me a long-distance cross-country runner. I suppose they thought I was just the build for it because I was long and skinny for my age (and still am) and in any case I didn't mind it too much, to tell you the truth, because running had always been made much of in my family, especially running away from the police.

The first two quotations are, of course, the opening lines of *Huckleberry Finn* (1885) and *The Catcher in the Rye* (1951). The connections between them are obvious, and have been frequently pointed out. But the connections between them and the third quotation, which is the opening of *The Loneliness of the Long-Distance Runner* (1959) by the young British writer Alan Sillitoe, are equally obvious. Allowing for the differences of speech determined by period and locale, all three passages adopt the same tone, establishing a direct, informal, conversational relationship between the narrator and the reader ("you"). All three exploit loose or "incorrect" grammar to subtle rhetorical effect, characteristically by adding to the end of a statement an unexpected qualification (Huck's "mainly", Holden's "but I don't feel like going into it", the runner's "especially running away from the police") that disconcerts yet delights us by its candour. All three, interestingly, invoke "truth" with deceptive casualness. In the face of adult incomprehension and adult evil, these youthful heroes are inventive and resourceful liars – but not to the reader: they are passionately concerned to find – and state – the truth. For this purpose the vernacular monologue is an ideal narrative method.

But the method has obvious limitations. The use of the first person necessarily excludes more than one perspective on events, while the use of the vernacular severely restricts the vocabulary and hence the expressive possibilities open to the writer. The above-mentioned writers get round this by using situational irony and the comments of other characters to evaluate their heroes, and by discreetly heightening the vernacular speech on occasion; but their freedom for manoeuvre of this kind is limited, and all successful attempts in this genre have the quality of a *tour de force*. Certain kinds of novelistic undertaking require either richer linguistic resources than those afforded by the vernacular, or a wider perspective than that afforded by the first person, or both.

What I have been discussing is, in literary parlance, "decorum": that is, the adjustment of style to subject, to the narrator and to the latter's assumed relationship to his audience. The interesting thing about American literature is that the vernacular monologue is virtually the only literary form in which decorum in this traditional sense is preserved. As soon as he leaves this mode, the American writer seems to be in a void of literary conventions, obliged to make up his own rules as he goes along. This may be observed by comparing Melville or Hawthorne with any major English novelist of the nineteenth century – Jane Austen, or Dickens, or George Eliot. The English novelists create and sustain their own distinctive authorial voices which give unity of form and feeling to their versions of experience, and persuade the reader to accept their validity. It may be an anonymous voice, but it is strongly charged with personality: urbane or energetic, jolly or meditative. It is always civilized and reliable. The reader knows where he is.

It is quite otherwise with the American writers. Melville threshes about in the literary conventions as wildly as his own white whale. The identifiable, if mysterious narrator who begins the story of *Moby Dick* fades gradually from view, and his function is taken over by an impersonal and omniscient narrator. The jocular, yarn-spinning style of the early chapters shifts into passages of prophetic declamation, Shakespearian pastiche, poetic lyricism, and discursive prose. Narrative alternates with dramatic dialogue, soliloquy and learned digression.

Hawthorne, though concerned, as Melville seems not to be, to cultivate an even and harmonious narrative tone, is scarcely less disconcerting. What he gives with one hand he seems to take away with the other. The supernatural is qualified by the sceptical, the symbolic by the literal. He keeps an anxious, wary eye on the reader. He takes a long time to warm up, but is given to effects of startling compression. His style is so highly polished it is almost painful. We can never relax in his presence.

One might speculate that literary decorum is not unconnected with social decorum in the ordinary sense of the word, and that the ease with which the English novelists find and sustain an appropriate tone owes something to the existence in England of a subtle and complex code of manners, understood and accepted by all, for which America has no equivalent. Similarly, American writing in the vernacular style may be interpreted as a rejection of attempts to import an alien code of manners into America. Its use of "low" and vulgar language, while preserving *literary* decorum, commonly draws protests from sections of the community committed to upholding conservative European standards of social decorum.

The American writer then, is, outside the vernacular monologue, fundamentally unsure about how to address himself to his subject and to his audience. As a result, he tends to fuse and combine modes of discourse – the prosaic, the lyrical, the satiric, the sentimental, the colloquial, the archaic, and the discursive – which in European literature are kept in separate compartments. To state it most simply: the American writer puts words together which, according to the canons of traditional literary decorum, just don't belong together. This can be most conveniently illustrated from poetry:

> Who goes there? Hankering, gross, mystical, nude?
> How is it I extract strength from the beef I eat?

One cannot imagine any English poet of the nineteenth century, including Hopkins, arranging that disturbing collocation of adjectives at the end of the first line, or springing that disconcerting question, an inch away from bathos, in the second. Whitman's lines have a distinctly modern ring; and when we consider that the modern poetic revolution in the English language was led by two Americans – T. S. Eliot and Ezra Pound – we may appreciate that the American writer's relative freedom from traditional canons of literary decorum brings with it tremendous advantages as well as disadvantages, particularly when it comes to the treatment of twentieth-century experience. This has been as true in fiction as in poetry.

If we apply Chase's descriptive distinction to twentieth-century fiction, we find it fits the American novel well enough, but the English novel not so well. The "powerful engrossing composition of wide ranges of experience into a normal centrality and equability of judgement" is essentially a characteristic of the eighteenth- and nineteenth-century novel, and its performance depended upon a way of life which, while fluid enough to be interesting, was also stable enough for the novelist to assume that he held in common with his audience essentially the same views on morals, metaphysics and society. Hence the ease with which the Victorian novelist sustained a tone that mingled a relaxed familiarity with a wise omniscience. He addressed himself to "the common reader", confident that such a person existed.

The twentieth century affords no such conditions, nor such confidence. The common reader, who never existed in America, is now, in England, only a ghost haunting book jackets. The modern novelist is conscious not of community, but of isolation, if not alienation. The experience he contemplates is fragmentary, disordered, subversive of the old certainties. This situation calls for a new kind of literary decorum, a decorum of indecorum, a bursting of the moulds of obsolete conventions, that yet avoids dissipating its energy in a welter of disconnected and contradictory effects.

The modern novelists may be judged by the success with which they have confronted this challenge. To me, the supreme example of success is Joyce's *Ulysses*, where language plays magically over the commonplace so as to stretch its significance to infinite dimensions, without, however, violating its value *as* the commonplace. Among other major novelists, Conrad projected his vision of the times in tales of adventure and melodrama overlaid with brooding philosophic scepticism and rich symbolic pattern; Virginia Woolf made the impossibility of communication her subject; D. H. Lawrence mingled the realistic and the visionary with a grand disdain for novelistic convention. Almost alone, E. M. Forster managed, precariously, to adapt the authorial manner of the nineteenth century to the matter of the twentieth. The novelists, like Galsworthy and Bennett, who went on writing as if nothing had happened, have not survived.

I am talking about the period of the "experimental" novel. But in America the novel had always been experimental, always groping, in profound uncertainty about its status and its audience, for new forms of expression with which to articulate baffling experience. Hence the language of modern American fiction – Hemingway's cunning manipulation of the simplest syntax and diction, Fitzgerald's lyricism so daringly expended upon the trivial and evanescent, Faulkner's torrential rhetoric, flecked with colloquialism – constituted less of a break with "tradition" than equivalent experiments in Europe – may indeed have been made possible by the absence of such a tradition.

The modern movement in literature seems to have lost much of its impetus. We are no longer living among giants. The contrast, however, is more striking in England than in America. In England we seem to be slipping back into old exhausted decorums, reverting to a Victorian technique based on a shallow or cynical assumption that class, material success and sexual behaviour still adequately contain the realities of existence. Style is all too well adjusted to this superficial view: English life being, on the surface, rather flat, dull and stuffy, we are producing a lot of novels written in flat, dull and stuffy prose. Leaving aside Graham Greene and Evelyn Waugh, who belong to an intermediate period I have not had space to touch on, the most interesting novelists we have are William Golding, who obtains poetic licence by only obliquely treating contemporary life, and Kingsley Amis, who makes comic capital out of the impoverishment of the contemporary English imagination. Otherwise only vernacular monologues, based on American models, relieve the monotony.

In America, however, it is still possible to sense that Joyce is a living influence. John Updike can make a golf shot into an epiphany; Bernard Malamud can treat the life of a baseball player, and J. F. Powers the life of a Catholic priest, in terms of Arthurian myth; Salinger can invest the apparatus of modern urban life with a strange significance, even blessedness. John Hawkes can turn a ride on a Greyhound bus into a macabre nightmare. These writers, in short, use language to slice deep into experience, not merely to pare the surface.

I am not suggesting that contemporary American novelists have solved all their problems. The lack of any tradition of literary decorum is still a liability as well as an asset. In those writers associated particularly with *The New Yorker*, the effort to submit the roughness and multiplicity of their material to the discipline of a measured and exact prose sometimes produces an effect of tortured preciousness, of strained urbanity, reminiscent of Hawthorne at his least happy moments. In what one might call the hipster wing of the American literary scene, embracing the Beats, Norman Mailer, William Burroughs, *et alii*, the traditional American indifference to decorum only encourages the fallacy that passionate commitment can compensate for formal incoherence, that "anything goes".

Saul Bellow's *Herzog* seems to me very representative of the strengths and weaknesses of contemporary American fiction. Whereas in British fiction today vitality seems to be exclusive to the uncouth, Herzog is alive *and* civilized, sensual *and* bookish. Bellow's nervously energetic prose, ransacking every level of contemporary English from slang to philosophical terminology, conveys a forceful impression of the multiplicity of modern consciousness, in which the sense of private and public crisis, of beauty mingled with squalor, of tenderness snatched out of horror, of tragedy wobbling on the brink of the absurd, are simultaneously present. This density of impression is felt particularly in the many superlative descriptions of Herzog's responses to the urban scene. But in the end one feels that Bellow overreaches himself, tries to make his hero bear the weight of too much meaning – or too much explicit meaning. In a very characteristically American way he seems impatient with the restraints of novelistic convention, and his urgent need to make his message heard and felt spills over into passages of unassimilated philosophizing.

Bellow strains, through bold metaphor and racy idiom, to make Herzog the vehicle for large generalizations about the plight of modern man. But the "ideas" remain ideas, with rather awkward demands upon our assent as ideas, and are not extensions of Herzog's character; and the effort to make Herzog measure up to their universality of reference betrays Bellow into a certain verbal excess, a desperate squandering of words bordering at times on incoherence. Bellow is not so much presenting his hero to the reader as colluding with his hero to impress the reader.

I am not enlisting in the currently fashionable pursuit of knocking *Herzog* because it is a popular success. The kind of flaw I find in it seems to me to run through a great deal of American literature and to be almost inseparable from what is vital in it. Certainly one must prefer a "failure" like *Herzog* to most "successes" in contemporary British fiction.

Mailer and Female (1971)

The Reviewer approached *The Prisoner of Sex** with a quickened heart-beat of keen expectation, but warily, unsure whether he hoped to find it a triumph or a failure. Norman Mailer was for his money one of the most interesting and entertaining of contemporary American writers, a man who had recovered from that direst of literary fates, the best-selling first novel followed by a string of failures, and by sheer effort and character remade himself as an artist in middle age. In particular the Reviewer admired semi-confessional, semi-documentary works, like *The Armies of the Night* and *Miami and the Siege of Chicago* in which Norman wrote about himself in the third person, as the Novelist, the Historian, the Journalist, thus achieving a delicious ironic detachment from his own ego without which indeed his matter and manner could become tiresomely pretentious and irresponsibly extreme.

Peeking into the opening pages of the new book, the Reviewer was glad to see that it was written in the ironic third-person mode, but he was well aware too of what polemical purpose it in this case served. The same cultural trade-winds that had brought across the Atlantic tidings of the growing strength of the movement for Women's Liberation, and the growing fame of its chief prophet, Kate Millett, had also conveyed whiffs of the excitement greeting Norman's counterblast, originally rushed to the public in a single issue of *Harper's* magazine, to Women's Lib in general and Kate Millett in particular. For Kate, in her monumental study of man's oppression of woman, *Sexual Politics*, had singled out Norman along with D. H. Lawrence and Henry Miller, as prime examples of male chauvinism in modern literature. The prospect

*N. Mailer, *The Prisoner of Sex* (Weidenfeld & Nicolson, 1971).

of Mailer counter-attacking was one to make the mouth water – but with an ambiguous flow of sympathies. After all, many of the Reviewer's best friends, including his wife, were in Women's Lib. He had read his Kate Millett, his Germaine Greer, his Eva Figes, etc., and while inclined to pick holes in the arguments here and there, to yawn a little over Millett and to skim Greer for the jokes, while deploring some of the planks (like abortion on demand) in the Women's Lib platform, and doubting some of their claims (such as that all sexual role-differences were behavioural, not structural, the reversible results of conditioning), while being unhappy about the way imaginative literature was used as evidence in the denunciation of male chauvinism (raising the spectre of a new kind of critical police-state to rival those already created by Marxists and Leavisites), though curious to know how many women first heard about the vaginal orgasm when it was denounced as a myth and a wicked masculine conspiracy, and wondering whether the freedom to leave one's infants in a twenty-four hour nursery, or at home with an obliging husband, in order to go out to work, was necessarily a liberation, given the nature of work for most people in a modern industrialized state – when all these reservations and qualifications had been made (the Reviewer, finding Norman's penchant for the long sentence infectious, drew a deep breath) the fact remained that the Movement was more right than wrong – women *were* on the whole oppressed, exploited and underprivileged *qua* women, and not just *qua* human beings.

Not the least persuasive support for this conclusion was the Reviewer's observation that women touched by the breath of Lib became more interesting *qua* women than they had been before. Some, indeed, became visible to him for the first time. He witnessed remarkable transformations among his female acquaintances, and if it all seemed at times like a wave of religious revivalism – initial scepticism and resistance in the unliberated woman suddenly giving way to a total conversion, public confession of former sins, eloquent witness to the grace of liberation and zeal in passing on the good news to others – well, that did not necessarily invalidate it, but rather suggested that orthodox religion had a formidable new force to reckon with. Not least the Roman Catholic Church, chief custodian of the two female archetypes (or stereotypes) most odious to the Liberationists: Eve and Mary – woman as sexual seductress, source of all man's troubles, and woman as meek and mild mother, man's submissive better half. The Church might be compared to an army in which all the officers were men and all the other ranks women (was not the definition of a good Catholic in many countries a man whose wife went to mass?) – imagine then the consequences of a mutiny of the troops. Well, there was a certain relish in that prospect. The celibacy of the clergy would seem a minor issue when the case for a female priesthood was properly opened; and the best hope for resolving the tiresome anomalies of the Church's teaching on birth control was for Catholic women to take the matter (which after all concerned them most) into their own hands.

In short, being a liberal or progressive Catholic, it seemed to the Reviewer, necessarily entailed a goodly measure of support for Women's Lib. But being a literary man, too, he didn't doubt for a moment that he would rather read Norman Mailer than Kate Millett any day of the week, including Sundays. Indeed, the early chapters of *The Prisoner of Sex* (delivered to the vacationing Reviewer by an unsuspecting Connemara postman whose hair would surely have stood on end had he known what a ticking time-bomb of four-letter words he held in his hands) were so brilliantly written, so funny, so eloquent, so artfully self-deprecating in defence, so metaphorically inventive in attack, that the Reviewer seriously began to think that Norman was going to carry the day and win a famous victory over General Millett and her indignant regiment of women. But gradually it became evident that even Norman did not believe he could win. It was Henry Miller he was referring to, but it might well have been himself, when he said about halfway through the book: "But the men moving silently in retreat all pass the prophet by. It is too late to know if he is right or wrong. The women have breached an enormous hole in the line, and the question is only how far back the men must go before they are ready to establish a front. Confusion is at the crossroads. Will D. H. Lawrence have to be surrendered as well?"

Actually (if I may drop the pastiche and speak directly) Mailer makes some good points on the level of literary criticism in defending Henry Miller and D. H. Lawrence against the strictures of Kate Millett. But when it comes to defending himself he chooses, with characteristic recklessness ("better to expire as a devil in the fire than as angel in the wings"), not to take cover behind the fictiveness of his writings, but to develop discursively and at length his idiosyncratic and highly vulnerable philosophy of sex. This includes such quaint notions as that women once possessed the power of "natural contraception" – an ability to conceive or not conceive according to their deepest needs and instincts (which might however – neat escape clause! – be opposite to their conscious wishes), an ability lost with the invention of artificial contraceptives which are in fact (because of the biological and psychological disturbance they cause) less reliable than the mysterious art of the past. Thus Mailer reaches the splendid paradox that contraception is responsible for the population explosion! Clearly the hardliners in the Catholic anti-contraception lobby (the *real* hardliners, not weak-kneed defenders of the Rhythm Method, "no more than a torturing of the egg" as Mailer vividly describes it) have found a surprising, and no doubt embarrassing new ally.

Norman Mailer, indeed, in the most heterodox possible way, is a religious fellow, a fervent believer in the devil and very apt to drop the name of the Lord in conversation. It is not the death of God that worries him, but the prospective death of Nature – killed by technology; and it is this sense of looming ecological disaster that provides the dynamic of his argument in *The Prisoner of Sex*. He equates the technological destruction of nature with the ideological destruction of male-female differentiation, likening Kate Millett to "a technologist who drains all the swamps only to discover that the ecological balance has been savaged", and himself proudly adopting the stance of a sexual Luddite. He highlights those passages in Millett and others which invoke the powers of science, especially in the field of genetic engineering, to liberate woman from her biology, discerning in this brave new world only a totalitarian nightmare: "The end-game of the absurd is coitus-free conception monitored by the state."

Polarized between Millett and Mailer, the debate over the liberation of women thus begins to fall into familiar patterns of utopian and anti-utopian speculation. And for those to whom the concept of Original Sin is still a meaningful one, there must be a deep appeal in Mailer's matter, however offensive his Rabelaisian manner may prove. For it is basically the idea of Original Sin that explains his title and justifies his obsession with sex as a novelist and as a man. "No thought was so painful [to the modern Enlightenment] as the idea that sex had meaning: for give meaning to sex and one was the prisoner of sex – the more meaning one gave it, the more it assumed, until every failure and misery, every evil of your life, spoke their lines in its light, and every fear of mediocre death."

But for all the rhetoric he musters to assert the heroism required to be fully a man, it is clear that the suffering and danger which Mailer cherishes as guarantees of human authenticity are, in the field of sexuality, mostly to be borne by women. That sex was existentially more meaningful when every act of love (for all the partners knew) might result in conception and/or the death of the woman in childbirth, is easily said (Mailer says it) because impossible to disprove; but it would be surprising if women were nostalgic for such good old days.

Norman Mailer, in other words, succumbs to the special temptation that waits upon anti-Pelagians: to accept the imperfections and evils of human life on behalf of others rather than of oneself. The liberation of women is something for women themselves to decide. Norman Mailer has the consolation of knowing that his book on the subject will survive most of theirs.

Family Romances (1975)

It is almost exactly ten years since *The New Yorker* published (on June 19, 1965) "Hapworth 16, 1924" by J. D. Salinger. That story, a further instalment in the saga of the Glass family which commenced back in 1948 with "A Perfect Day for Bananafish", itself broke a silence of six years following the publication of "Seymour: an introduction" in June 1959. Since "Hapworth" Salinger has published nothing.

Ten years in literature is not as long as ten years in politics, but it is a long enough time in which to be forgotten, especially if your silence is total. Salinger's eremitic seclusion, his fanatical defence of his privacy, are of course well known – and while he was still publishing merely intensified public interest in him. Since he stopped publishing, however, his shunning of publicity has ceased to be noteworthy. To say he has been forgotten would not be quite accurate: his works are still in print and evidently sell steadily, especially *The Catcher in the Rye*, which seems assured of some kind of classic status. Rather, it is as if he had died. His name no longer sets off vibrations of expectancy and curiosity among readers of modern fiction. It seems to be generally assumed that his career is a closed chapter, belonging to the literary history of the 1950s; that his interesting and original talent fizzled out disappointingly in the 1960s and was swamped by a new wave of American fiction quite different in character.

A few months ago, however, Salinger broke his long silence and revealed that it may yet prove to be a pregnant one. In a telephone conversation with Lacey Fosburgh of *The New York Times* he stated that he was still writing busily, though not for publication. "There is a marvellous peace in not publishing," he said. "I love to write. But I write for myself and my own pleasure" (*New York Times*,

November 3, 1974). What provoked this communiqué was the pirated publication in the United States of *The Complete Uncollected Short Stories of J. D. Salinger*, in two volumes.

These paperbacks, quite decently printed, though not very well proof read and badly bound, were evidently hawked around the bookshops of San Francisco and other large cities by various young men all using the alias of Greenburg, and an estimated 25,000 sets have been sold at retail prices ranging from $3 to $5 a volume. At the time of the interview the pirates had not been traced, and Salinger was suing the bookshops.

It is, of course, deplorable that a writer's work should be reprinted against his will, quite apart from the financial robbery involved. With the exception of "Hapworth", all the uncollected stories are early work, and one understands Salinger's wish to let "them die a perfectly natural death". On the other hand, it is never possible to "unwrite" something that has once been published (perhaps this is why Salinger finds not publishing so peaceful), and all the pirated stories are available for inspection in large libraries.

Even the most immature of them have the uncanny, hypnotic readability that is the hallmark of his writing, while a few of them would not have disgraced *Nine Stories*. But perhaps the most interesting discovery to be made by investigating the uncollected stories is that from an early stage in his career Salinger was using the short story as a way of exploring a complex network of relationships between *families* of characters; and that although he is thought of as pre-eminently the literary voice of the post-Second World War younger generation, his earliest work (naturally enough when you recall that he was born in 1919) was written from a pre-war or wartime perspective.

Holden Caulfield, the teenage hero of *The Catcher in the Rye* (1951), was first referred to, though he did not actually appear, in a story called "Last Day of the Last Furlough" (1944) which is about two young soldiers on the eve of a wartime posting overseas: John F. "Babe" Gladwaller and his friend Vincent Caulfield, who

> has a kid brother in the Army who flunked out of a lot of schools. He talks about him a lot. Always pretending to pass him off as a nutty kid.

This brother is called Holden and is "missing".

Another story, a very good one called "This Sandwich Has No Mayonnaise" (1945), is told from the point of view of Vincent unsuccessfully trying to suppress his misery and anxiety about Holden's fate in the Pacific:

> Stop kidding around. Stop letting people think you're Missing. Stop wearing my robe to the beach. Stop taking the shots on my side of the court. Stop whistling. Sit up to the table.

Some of Vincent's reminiscences include his sister Phoebe Caulfield. In "The Stranger" (1945), Babe Gladwaller (who has a Holden-Phoebe relationship of his own with his kid sister Mattie) describes Vincent's death in action to the latter's ex-girlfriend, who says that Vincent "didn't believe anything from the time little Kenneth Caulfield died. His brother." Kenneth seems to be the first version of Holden Caulfield's deceased younger brother Allie, about whose baseball mitt Holden writes an essay assignment for the ungrateful Stradlater in *The Catcher in the Rye*. Allie, however, died on July 18, 1946, and the Holden of the novel is a post-war teenager.

Between these stories and *The Catcher in the Rye* came two directly about Holden. "I'm Crazy" (1945) and "Slight Rebellion off Madison" (1946), which were incorporated, greatly expanded, into the novel. There are no specific historical references in these stories, but it seems to me, given the dates of their original publication, that a pre-war setting was implied. Salinger's unwillingness to reprint any of the early stories about the Caulfields no doubt derives partly from a wish to conceal their various inconsistencies with *The Catcher in the Rye*.

In the stories I have mentioned one can see an embryonic family saga of the Glass type beginning to emerge: there are the same intense sibling relationships, the same quasi-religious pursuit by the central characters of integrity, purity and authenticity in ordinary living, the same struggle against alienation. Salinger, it seems, having changed his mind too often about the Caulfields, abandoned that family's history, and started afresh with the Glasses – beginning characteristically by killing off his main character, Seymour (in "Bananafish"), and working outwards from that point, just as he had begun with Holden "missing". The question of period is settled by making Buddy Glass, the family scribe, the same age as Salinger himself. The formative years of Buddy and Seymour (two years his senior) are thus pre-war; but the size of the family means that the younger siblings, Zooey and Franny, can represent (as did Holden Mark II) the sensibility of post-war youth. The Caulfields, in fact, are not totally forgotten in the Glass saga. Buddy recalls in "Seymour":

> There used to be an exceptionally intelligent and likeable boy on the radio with S. and me – one Curtis Caulfield, who was eventually killed during one of the landings in the Pacific.

Buddy also alludes to the one novel he has published in terms which make it sound very like *The Catcher in the Rye*.

These teasing references, which deliberately entangle the myths of the Caulfields and the Glasses both with each other and with the historical J. D. Salinger, are typical of the writer's later work, where he is playing an elaborate game with his audience and with the conventions of his art. The name of the game is Assent. The more truth-telling, the more historical, the stories become in form (i.e. tending towards an apparently random, anecdotal structure, adopting an insistently personal, intimate, confessional tone, making elaborate play with letters, documents and similar "evidence"), the less credible becomes the content (miraculous feats of learning, stigmata, prophetic glimpses, memories of previous incarnations etc). Purporting to tell us a "true" family history, and dropping heavy hints that he is the same person as J. D. Salinger, Buddy yet insists again and again on the autonomy of art and the irrelevance of biographical criticism. An extravagantly transcendental philosophy of life is put forward in terms of studied homeliness, wrapped around with elaborate qualifications, disclaimers, nods and winks, and mediated in a style that, for all its restless rhetorical activity, is strikingly lacking in any kind of "poetic" or symbolist resonances. With each successive story, Salinger has raised the stakes in the game of Assent, and each time more and more readers have dropped out, unable to take the mysticism, the ESP, the God-knowingness at their face value. But what is it we are asked to believe in: the reality of these things, or the possibility of them? Clearly, since we are reading fiction, the latter; but it is easy to be confused by Salinger's method into thinking it is the former. To do so is to forfeit half the pleasure of reading him.

Unlikely as the comparison may seem at first glance, there is a certain similarity between the Salinger of "Zooey", "Raise High the Roofbeam, Carpenters" and "Seymour: an introduction" and Sterne's *Tristram Shandy*, that eighteenth-century "prose home-movie". In both there is a delicate balance of sentiment and ironic self-consciousness, and a humorous running commentary on the activities of writing and reading. How Shandean, for instance, is Buddy's presentation to the reader, in "Seymour", of

> this unpretentious bouquet of very early-blooming parentheses: (((( )))). I suppose, most unflorally, I truly mean them to be taken, first off, as bow-legged – buckle-legged – omens of my state of mind and body at this writing.

One of the disappointments of "Hapworth" is that it lacks this teasing, cajoling relationship with the reader. Apart from a brief prologue and epilogue by Buddy, it consists of an inordinately long letter written by Seymour at the age of seven to his parents, from a summer camp. It is, needless to say, an extraordinarily precocious epistle, full of wise moralizing, advice, injunctions and prophecies, and concludes with a request for library books by Tolstoy, Cervantes, Dickens, George Eliot, Thackeray, Jane Austen, Bunyan, the Brontës, Victor Hugo, Balzac,

Flaubert, Maupassant, Proust, and many others, each plea accompanied by a crisp if idiosyncratic critical appraisal of the author in question.

It is another, audacious ploy in the game of Assent; but although Salinger has skilfully fabricated a prose style that is just what you would expect from a prodigy like Seymour – preciously adult in syntax and diction, but not quite sure of its tone, and liable to sudden drops into childish vernacular – this is not quite enough to conceal the fact that Seymour is really a rather boring character (it is what others make of him that is interesting). Also, Seymour's somewhat fulsome enthusiasm for his younger brother's literary promise, unqualified by any ironic commentary from Buddy himself, is a little hard to take. Instead of the dialogue between writer and reader that animates the three preceding stories, we seem to be overhearing a self-congratulatory dialogue of the writer with himself. That is why, although it is good news that Salinger is still writing, one feels misgivings at the reported words, "I write just for myself and my own pleasure."

If "Hapworth" does not offer much cheer to faithful fans of Salinger, it no doubt brings a glow of righteous justification to those critics who detected a dangerous narcissism, or Pygmalionism, in the Glass stories as early as "Franny" and "Zooey". Yet it is a real question how far they contributed to the fulfilment of their own prophecies. Looking through H. A. Grunwald's useful collection of comment and criticism, *Salinger* (1962), it is clear that most critics turned against Salinger just when his work began to challenge customary modes of reading; while Salinger's dedication of his last volume to "an amateur reader" if there is one "still left in the world" suggests a growing sense of desertion.

Whatever the reason, it seems a shame that so gifted a writer – probably the first since Hemingway to discover a wholly original mode of writing short stories – should have retreated into silent self-communing. No one, except a few cultural chauvinists and Mr Kingsley Amis giving his well-known impersonation of Evelyn Waugh, would seriously dispute the brilliance, the imaginative energy and daring of American fiction over the past ten or fifteen years. But there are moments (one might occur on reading page 235 of Pynchon's *Gravity's Rainbow* where the girl is defecating into the open mouth of Brigadier Pudding and you realize there are five hundred pages still to go) when the reader may look back wistfully to the economy, the delicacy, the artful mimicry, the tenderly ironic domesticity, the goddam *reticence*, if you want to know the truth, of vintage Salinger.

Fitzgerald's Fear of the Flesh (1978)

F. Scott Fitzgerald was born into an Irish-American Catholic family, and his early life was permeated by Catholic influences at home and at school. After experiencing the repressive and provincial Catholic subculture of St Paul, Minnesota, he was exposed to a more glamorous and sophisticated version of his religion through his mentor Monsignor Cyril Fay and Shane Leslie, who was a teacher at his Catholic preparatory school in the East. For many years, up till the time he fell in love with Zelda, Fitzgerald himself flirted with the idea of becoming a priest.

These facts are not new discoveries, but Joan M. Allen* believes their significance for the interpretation of Scott Fitzgerald's fiction has been underestimated, perhaps because the novelist himself played them down in deference to his predominantly Wasp readership. She argues that Fitzgerald's religious background is indeed a key to the special preoccupations and obsessions she finds in his work:

> his prominent theme of parents' failure to nurture the spirit of their children, his heroes who either adopt surrogate fathers who are priests or assume the priestly role themselves, his viciously destructive women who wear masks designed to hide their essential insidiousness, his men who allow themselves to be emasculated by these fascinating destroyers, the abundant squeamishness about sex in a writer proclaimed as risqué and shocking, the ubiquitous carnival imagery in his writing . . .

This approach to Fitzgerald is most plausible as it applies to his treatment of sexuality, and especially in his early immature work. The

* J. M. Allen, *Candles and Carnival Lights: The Catholic Sensibility of F. Scott Fitzgerald* (New York University Press, 1978).

hero's encounters with women in *This Side of Paradise*, for example, very clearly exemplify that polarization of women into the Eve-seductress figure and the Virgin Mother figure which Catholic culture tends to implant in the minds of its sons. In *The Beautiful and the Damned* the hero teases a girlfriend with the story of the Chevalier O'Keefe, a Catholic gentleman of old who, plagued by temptations of the flesh, retreated to a monastery where he would be safely out of harm's way, confined perpetually to a cell high up in a tower; but on his way up the staircase he caught sight of a pretty girl outside adjusting her stocking, and in his eagerness to see her legs fell out of the window to his death in a state of sin – indeed, being deemed to have committed suicide, he was even denied a Christian burial. This hilarious parody of Catholic cautionary tales could only have been invented by someone who once took them seriously, and indeed the hero himself does not seem entirely flippant in relating it.

Fear of the destructive power of sex and of women as its vehicles persists in Fitzgerald's mature work, but in more subtle and complex forms. As Leslie Fiedler has noted, the Dark Lady and the Fair Lady are different sides of the same person in the characters of Daisy in *The Great Gatsby* and of Nicole in *Tender is the Night*; and the concept of sin becomes less theological, certainly less eschatological, in those novels than in the earlier ones. Thus, while Ms Allen is an instructive and illuminating guide to Fitzgerald's early life and work, there is less material for her purposes in the work of his maturity, in discussing which she is forced back on some rather routine tracing of submerged religious symbolism and allusion.

One might venture the hypothesis that Fitzgerald's coming of age as a novelist entailed not just personally repudiating Catholic dogma and religious practice (as did Joyce, while continuing to write about it) but virtually eliminating all overt Catholic reference from his fiction. In this respect the story "Absolution", originally the cancelled first chapter of *The Great Gatsby*, Fitzgerald's one masterpiece, is of crucial interest, and Ms Allen's account of it will no doubt prompt other readers besides myself to look it up.

Fitzgerald evidently intended the story to be the account of a turning point in the adolescent life of Jay Gatsby (here called Rudolph Miller). The dreamy, rebellious son of a strict and devout Catholic father in a "Swede town" in the Mid-West, Rudolph gets himself into a spiritual tangle of casuistry and superstition entirely typical of pre-Conciliar Catholicism. Compelled to confess his slight but shaming sins of impurity, he tells a lie which renders the sacrament inefficacious. Next day, prevented by his father from deliberately breaking his fast (which would enable him to avoid taking the Eucharist) he is forced to make what he believes to be a sacrilegious communion.

This story is framed by Rudolph's interview with the priest Father Schwartz, to whom he comes for counsel in his spiritual crisis. Schwartz himself, however, is in torments of sexual temptation, maddened by the summer heat, the smell of cheap toilet soap from the drug store, the knowing laughter of young girls passing under his window. So far from counselling the young boy, he reveals the turmoil of his own inner life in an incoherent outpouring of cryptic hints and warnings. The boy is both frightened and elated – "absolved" from his guilt by a new secular awareness: "Underneath his terror he felt that his own inner convictions were confirmed. There was something ineffably gorgeous somewhere that had nothing to do with God."

Clearly, in Fitzgerald's original conception, this was to be the origin of Jay Gatsby's quest for the American Dream; yet I doubt whether any reader, without being told, would guess that "Absolution" was ever part of the conception of *The Great Gatsby*. Not only did Fitzgerald eliminate specifically Catholic associations from Jay Gatsby's early life – he also adopted an entirely different (and much more sophisticated) narrative technique from the one he had used in "Absolution". Instead of an over-explicit third-person narrative that moves clumsily between the consciousnesses of the main figures in the story (as in most of Fitzgerald's early fiction) he adopted the more oblique method of a characterized first-person narrator (Nick Carroway), and he exploited flashback and ellipsis much more boldly in the temporal organization of the narrative. The effect was that Gatsby became a much more mythical and mysterious figure, an enigma into which one may read many possible meanings, rather than a semi-autobiographical hero struggling to transcend specifically Catholic social and cultural origins. The literary gain was enormous.

"Absolution" may also give us a clue to Fitzgerald's curious obsession with kissing – his tendency, noted by Fiedler, to make osculation rather than genital sex the point of erotic climax for his characters, and the occasion, very often, for expressing that "squeamishness" noted by Ms Allen. This is particularly, almost absurdly, striking in *This Side of Paradise*, in which the early scene of the pubescent hero's first kiss – "He had never kissed a girl before, and he tasted his lips, curiously, as if he had munched some new fruit", immediately followed by feelings of "sudden revulsion . . . disgust, loathing" – establishes a pattern that is repeated again and again. The metaphorical "fruit" here is pretty obviously the one Eve offered to Adam, and Fitzgerald seems to have gone on believing, long after he had lapsed from the Catholic Church, that kissing involved the breaking of some solemn taboo, and a fall from grace and innocence for the participants. "Gatsby's heart beat faster and faster as Daisy's white face came up to his own. He knew that when he kissed this girl, and forever wed his unutterable visions to her perishable breath, his mind would never romp again like the mind of God."

The young boy in "Absolution" has a vivid premonition of the consequences of making a sacrilegious communion: "Communion taken upon an uncleansed soul would turn to poison in his mouth, and he would crumple limp and damned from the altar-rail." Could this association of the mouth with the reception of the consecrated host explain why the erotic kiss was charged with such excitement and dread for Fitzgerald? Ms Allen records that a girl who met him in 1917, and found him lacking in aggressive male sexuality, observed: "His mouth was his most revealing feature . . . All his Midwestern puritanism was there." All his Catholic hang-ups about flesh and spirit, too, perhaps; for Fitzgerald's Midwestern puritanism was specifically Catholic, and Ms Allen has done well to remind us of that important fact. *Candles and Carnival Lights* is not epoch-making, but it makes a genuine point thoughtfully, lucidly, and responsibly.

The Limits of the Movement (1980)

The terms that label periods in literary history or that group together writers of a particular time deemed to have had certain aims in common – terms such as Augustan, Romantic, Decadent, Imagist, and so on – are necessarily imprecise, inevitably distorting, and always open to challenge (often by the very writers to whom they are applied). But criticism cannot do without such concepts, since it is only by means of them that the bewildering mass of literary data can be reduced to an intelligible order – the order of literary history. One might go further and say that the institution of literature itself depends for its health on the currency of these descriptive terms. If the English literary scene in the last decade has seemed to many observers rather dull, part of the reason may have been the failure of the good writers we have to find common ground between themselves, or the failure of criticism to make them collectively visible. As Henry James memorably said, "Art lives upon discussion, upon experiment, upon curiosity, upon variety of attempt, upon the exchange of views and the comparison of standpoints"; but such debate is likely to be most productive when the issues are sharply focused by a dominant school or movement.

Arguably the last literary movement to manifest itself in England was that which emerged in the 1950s and was called simply the "Movement". In the 1960s, to be sure, there was a general cultural revolution – the "countercultural" mix of drugs, rock music, flower-power, hippiedom, happenings and radical politics – which had its effect on writing while being itself essentially non-literary in orientation; and there have been since the 1950s small groups or groupings of writers, such as the poetry "Group" presided over by Edward Lucie-Smith and Philip Hobsbaum, or the Liverpool poets, or today's young political playwrights, Howard Brenton, David Hare and Trevor Griffiths. But the mid-1950s was the last time when a considerable number of like-minded writers joined forces, or were seen to be doing so (which is almost the same thing in literary politics), to give a decisively new direction to British writing – to found, in the jargon of contemporary French criticism, a new *écriture*. That phenomenon is the subject of a very thorough historical and critical study by Blake Morrison.*

What was the Movement, and who was in it? It was effectively launched in 1954 by the literary editor of the *Spectator*, J. D. Scott, who, with the conscious motive of calling attention to his paper, wrote a provocative, coat-trailing, trend-spotting editorial entitled "In The Movement", which was published (anonymously) in the issue of 1 October. In this article Scott discussed the group of young poets already identified by another *Spectator* writer, Anthony Hartley, as having certain qualities in common – academicism, anti-romanticism, hard-headed common sense – which distinguished them from the Modernist tradition, and he suggested that the same literary values were making themselves felt in prose fiction with the publication of lively first novels by two of these poets – John Wain's *Hurry on Down* and Kingsley Amis's *Lucky Jim*. Scott argued that these new young writers were reflecting, in their work, real changes in British society, and were destined to supersede the rather weary and washed-out custodians of the modernist-bohemian-cosmopolitan high cultural tradition who had controlled the literary market-place since the Second World War.

> The Movement . . . is bored by the despair of the Forties, not much interested in suffering, and extremely impatient of poetic sensibility . . . So it's goodbye to all those rather sad little discussions about "how the writer ought to live", and it's goodbye to the Little Magazine and "experimental writing". The Movement as well as being anti-phoney, is anti-wet; sceptical, robust, ironic, prepared to be as comfortable as possible . . .

The Movement was thus rather fortuitously christened and launched, but, as Blake Morrison rightly insists, it was not a journalistic invention. Scott's original article caused a stir because it crystallized the hunches and intuitions of many observers of the literary scene, that a new generation of writers was emerging with a distinctive collective voice. A couple of years later the reality of the Movement, at least as far as poetry was concerned, was convincingly established by the publication of Robert Conquest's anthology *New Lines* (1956). This presented the

* B. Morrison, *The Movement: English Poetry and Fiction of the 1950s* (Oxford University Press, 1980).

work of nine poets: Elizabeth Jennings, John Holloway, Philip Larkin, Thom Gunn, Kingsley Amis, D. J. Enright, Donald Davie, John Wain and Conquest himself. It was prefaced by a terse, coolly confident editorial introduction presenting this work as "a genuine and healthy poetry of the new period".

Although Conquest did not actually use the word "Movement" in his introduction, *New Lines* came to be seen as the quintessential Movement anthology, and Al Alvarez certainly treated it as such when he came to launch his own counter-revolutionary anthology, *The New Poetry*, in 1962. (It is, incidentally, significant that Alvarez was unable to identify a new school of native poets, but was obliged to field a rather oddly assorted team of Britons and Americans.) The application of the term "Movement" to prose fiction was always more problematical and uncertain, and no one, to my knowledge, ever applied it to drama; but there were certainly connections and overlappings between Movement poetry, strictly defined, and other new writing in the 1950s. The typical Movement poet was a university teacher of lower-middle-class origins living in a provincial city, and the fiction of William Cooper and C. P. Snow could be said to reflect a very similar ethos and milieu. Indeed, Amis acknowledged the seminal influence of Cooper's *Scenes From Provincial Life* (1950), and as a reviewer of new novels in the newspapers, as well as in his own literary practice, Cooper's friend Snow reinforced the Movement's anti-modernist aesthetic. The consciously provincial and anti-bourgeois attitudes expressed in this fiction allowed it to be associated with much rougher, rawer novels and plays more aggressively critical of British society, such as Alan Sillitoe's *Saturday Night and Sunday Morning* (1958), John Braine's *Room at the Top* (1957) and John Osborne's *Look Back in Anger* (1956). A new kind of hero, or antihero, was hailed and dubbed the Angry Young Man – a journalistic term which proved sufficiently elastic to be stretched around not only characters like Jimmy Porter, Arthur Seaton and Jim Dixon, but also their creators, and finally any brash young newcomer to the literary scene.

Thus two writers as different and mutually unsympathetic as, say, Kingsley Amis and Colin (*The Outsider*) Wilson, could be bundled into the same category. All this has more to do, perhaps, with the history of publicity than of literature, but as Donald Davie, one of the core members of the Movement (and one of the most puritanical in values) has acknowledged, "Promotion is of the nature of any artistic move-ment." It was the achievement of the original Movementeers – especially Amis, Wain, Larkin, Davie, Enright, Holloway and Conquest – to start rolling a small, tightly packed snowball which, as it grew, gathered irresistible momentum, and picked up on its course a good deal of heterogeneous and incongruous matter.

Like all new literary movements, the Movement was essentially Oedipal in its efforts at self-definition, attacking the aims and methods of the preceding literary generation: the heavily symbolic and often wilfully obscure poetry of Dylan Thomas and other bards of the "New Apocalypse" (neatly parodied by Wain in *Hurry on Down* and by Amis in *That Uncertain Feeling*) and, in prose fiction, the sombre spiritual and emotional intensities of Graham Greene. Jim Dixon scornfully recalls "a character in a modern novel Beesley had lent him who was always feeling pity moving in him like a sickness or some such jargon" – an allusion for the knowing reader to *The Heart of the Matter*, though as Blake Morrison observes, Amis carefully ensures that his hero is not caught out dropping the names of the books he has read (still less pretending to have *bought* a modern novel).

This was part of the deliberate cultivation of the "common touch" by the Movement writers – their refusal to be awed by the conventional cultural tastes and values of the educated bourgeoisie (advertising their preference for jazz over Mozart and madrigals) and their horror of anything that smacked of highbrow affectation or showing off. Their spiritual mentor in this regard – and the only literary father-figure, apart from Empson and Graves, for whom they had much respect – was George Orwell, whose brave, often unpopular stand in the 1930s and 1940s for human decency against totalitarian ideologies they respected, and whose colloquial, no-nonsense, "truth-telling" literary style they imitated in fiction and criticism.

Thirties' writing in Britain, ostensibly committed to the cause of the proletariat, was in fact, as Orwell frequently pointed out, dominated by a group of upper-middle-class young men who had all been to prep schools and public schools together, and in many cases went back to teach in them after Oxbridge, if they did not find comfortable niches in the London literary world. The Movement writers also went to Oxbridge, but they got there by winning scholarships from grammar schools, and they went on to teach at the redbrick universities that were rapidly expanding under the impetus of the 1944 Education Act: Amis at Swansea, Enright at Birmingham, Holloway at Aberdeen, Wain at Reading, and Larkin (as librarian) at Belfast. Davie taught at patrician, but provincial, Trinity College, Dublin, and maintained that the sociological significance of the Movement was very great because "for the first time a challenge is thrown down, not by individuals . . . but by a more or less coherent group, to the monopoly of British culture sustained for generations by the London haute-bourgeoisie".

A single episode in Blake Morrison's chronicle of the Movement epitomizes this transfer of power. Early in 1953, John Lehmann, whose editorial and publishing activities had exerted powerful influence on

English literary life from the late 1930s to the early 1950s, learned that his contract as editor of the BBC Third Programme's programme "New Soundings", a platform for new writing, was not to be renewed. He was replaced by one of his own contributors, John Wain, who renamed the programme "First Reading". Philip Larkin subsequently observed that "the Movement, if you want to call it that, really began when John Wain succeeded John Lehmann on that BBC programme." One of John Wain's early novels was called *Strike the Father Dead*.

My own career as a writer – if I may be personal for a moment – was launched very much on the back of the wave started by the Movement, though I was only dimly conscious of this at the time. First of all, the Movement, and the "snowball effect" it had on the literary scene at large, created a mood receptive and encouraging to young aspiring writers: there was a sense of excitement and expectation about literature and drama in England in those days which has not been generated since – and which is not, I think, simply the illusion of middle age looking back at its youth. And to get into this new literary scene one did not need the advantages of a privileged, cultured background, or to have exotic, unconventional or heroic experience to write about. A lower-middle-class South London suburban upbringing, such as I had, was suddenly an almost fashionable background for a young novelist – though not quite as fashionable as a working-class upbringing in a Northern industrial town.

When J. D. Scott's article "In The Movement" appeared in the *Spectator* in the autumn of 1954, I was beginning my final year as an undergraduate reading English (only we did not say "reading", we said "doing") at University College, London, and too preoccupied with *Beowulf*, Chaucer, and other classics of English literature to take much notice of contemporary writing.

I still cherished rather romantic notions of the life-style appropriate to a writer, and on this account piously declined to apply for a state studentship to do research. When I was subsequently offered a university research studentship, I postponed the decision while I did National Service in the Army. A few weeks of basic training at Catterick convinced me that the academic life had a lot to be said for it, and the longer my National Servitude (as I saw it) went on, the stronger grew my resolve to return to the university. This was a decision very much in the spirit, if not the letter, of *Lucky Jim*, and its hero's axiom, "nice things are nicer than nasty things". It also started me on a twin career – as a university teacher of English and as a novelist – which the Movement, notably in the persons of Amis, Wain and Enright, had established as viable. There had been poet-dons before the Movement, of course – I. A. Richards and William Empson spring to mind – but not, if one excludes writers of detective stories, fantasy and historical fiction, novelist-dons.

I whiled away the long boredom of clerking at a Royal Armoured Corps training centre in Dorset by compiling a scrapbook of literary cuttings from newspapers and magazines, and by writing the first draft of a novel called *The Picturegoers*, in which scenes of Catholic "ghetto" life were crosscut with vignettes of mass cultural consumption at a seedy suburban cinema – a project that reflected the incongruous influences of Graham Greene and Richard Hoggart, whose *The Uses of Literacy* (1957) was, in its Leavisian critical principles and eloquent celebration of provincial working-class life, tangentially related to the Movement. When *The Picturegoers* was published after some delays, in 1960, among the reviewers who gave it a kind welcome were two contributors to *New Lines* – Kingsley Amis (in the *Observer*) and Elizabeth Jennings (in the *Listener*).

With this background, it is hardly necessary to say that I approached Blake Morrison's study of the Movement with keen interest; and I finished it with a great respect for his scholarship. He has meticulously traced the various converging influences that made up the Movement sensibility and stance: Orwell and Empson; Graves and Hardy; Logical Positivism and Leavis; grammar school and austerity Oxbridge.

He has identified the verbal devices that create the characteristic tone of Movement verse – for example, the lavish use of the first person plural pronoun which allows the poet simultaneously to address a coterie audience of fellow dons and to claim solidarity with a wider audience of ordinary "chaps"; and the hesitant qualifiers and interrogatives – "perhaps", "no, that's not", "more a", "is it?" and so on – which guarantee the sincerity and authenticity of the poet's thinking. Mr Morrison has an eagle eye for poetic echoes (spotting Sassoon's to *shake off dread*, from the *Georgian Anthology*, for instance, in Larkin's *shaking off the dread* in "Mr Bleaney"). He traces all the relevant lines of friendship and professional association that connected the various Movement writers with each other. He seems to have missed nothing, and I could fault him on only one textual interpretation – a strained misreading of the last verse of Amis's "Autobiographical Fragment". Yet the book left me feeling slightly flat, slightly disappointed, for reasons that are I think partly the Movement's fault, and partly Mr Morrison's.

He claims that the Movement was probably the most influential literary group in England since the Imagists. If this is even half true (and the claims of the Auden-Isherwood group are surely at least as strong) then a reader who knew the work of the Movement only from this study might be very puzzled to understand why. Of the writers discussed, only Larkin emerges as a writer of real distinction: his lines shine from the page with a classic grace and poise that are all the more impressive for being wrested from superficially unpromising subject matter and diction. Mr Morrison's careful commentaries do Larkin justice, but he does not make out a very convincing case for any other Movement poet, nor do they show to advantage in the quotations he gives. This is even more true of his treatment of prose fiction. The sublime and liberating humour of Amis at his best, for instance, is not acknowledged or illustrated here.

Indeed, Mr Morrison is much more persuasive when he is pointing out the limitations and contradictions of the Movement, rather than its strengths. He deftly uncovers that yearning respect and admiration for values and virtues traditionally associated with social privilege that was hidden behind the surface rebelliousness and iconoclasm of the Movement writers, and which became quite explicit in their later work. (Their notorious shift to the Right should indeed have come as no surprise: J. D. Scott's characterization of the Movement as "anti-phoney . . . anti-wet; sceptical; robust, ironic, prepared to be as comfortable as possible" sounds very like a *Telegraph* eulogy of the Thatcher faction of the Tory Party.) He notes, and illustrates, the often dismaying crudity of Movement discussion of aesthetic matters. The flaunted philistinism which they used so effectively against literary pretentiousness was always a dangerous ploy: once the tongue is removed from the cheek, once the wit is relaxed and the element of surprise is lost, one is left with – just philistinism.

The Movement was indeed important, and, for reasons I have glanced at, my own particular generation of English writers – the first fruits of the 1944 Education Act – has reason to feel grateful to it for opening up the English literary world and making it accessible to us. Nevertheless it is impossible to suppress certain doubts and regrets about the narrowness of the Movement aesthetic (or anti-aesthetic) and the constraints it placed upon the subsequent development of many of its best writers, and therefore upon the development of English writing generally.

Donald Davie grew increasingly restive under these constraints and finally rebelled against them ("'The metaphysicality/Of Poetry, how I need it,/Yet it was for years/What I refused to credit") but the break was not a clean one, and Blake Morrison's quotations from Davie's later criticism show him deeply divided between the values of the conservative English poetic tradition and the cosmopolitan, experimental, Modernist one. Thom Gunn's emigration to America has been perhaps more complete, spiritually as well as physically, than Davie's, but his allegiance to the Movement was always problematical, as was Elizabeth Jennings's. John Holloway moved from Aberdeen to Cambridge and seemed to get increasingly absorbed by academic concerns rather than the wider stage of literary politics. As for the other founder-members of the Movement, although they initiated a fruitful co-operation between academic English studies and creative writing, they have since renounced the project, expressing various degrees of disillusionment or disgust with the rapid expansion of higher education in the humanities and the corresponding growth of academic literary criticism, and have adopted a defiantly protectionist, Little-Englander stance towards the theory and practice of new kinds of writing emanating from Europe and America. The Movement has not moved with the times. This may be a sign of integrity, but it could also be a symptom of arteriosclerosis.

Suck Cess (1978)

Martin Amis's first novel, *The Rachel Papers* (1973), was a very funny, scandalously explicit story of teenage sexuality in the Permissive Society, upper-middle-class division. The narrator, a jaded roué of twenty, looked back with appalled fascination at his younger self, a creature compelled by his insatiable flesh to pursue sexual satisfaction far beyond the limit of pleasure. The novel was remarkable for its description of foreplay and copulation in which the language of pleasure was exchanged for the language of painful labour, and in which anxiety, embarrassment and boredom swamped any feelings of satisfaction or tenderness. The overall impression left by the book was of an almost Swiftian horror at the nastiness of the human body and its needs (one chapter is called "Celia Shits" in conscious homage) which in the absence of any possible faith in Reason or Religion sought relief in a style of comic repartee perceptibly derivative from Amis *père*, e.g.:

> The hall smelled of boiling cabbage – or, let's be accurate, it smelled as if someone had eaten six bushels of asparagus, washed them down with as many quarts of Guinness, and pissed over the walls, ceiling and floor.

The stylistic echoes of Kingsley Amis were not surprising (it is hard enough for comic novelists not carrying his genes to avoid imitating him) but the tone was disturbingly different. Compare Lucky Jim waking up to a hangover ("His mouth had been used as a latrine by some small creature of the night, and then as its mausoleum") to Charles Highway waking up to symptoms of clap:

> on the following Friday or thereabouts I woke up to find that someone had squeezed a family-sized tube of pus all over my pyjama bottoms.

Jim Dixon was engagingly devoted to the principle that "nice things are nicer than nasty things"; but Charles Highway observes: "Surely nice things are dull and nasty things are funny. The nastier a thing is, the funnier it gets."

For many people (including the editor of the New Fiction Society's magazine, over whose protesting head it was made a Society choice) the nastiness of Martin Amis's second novel, *Dead Babies* (1975), was beyond a joke. Even the title was too offensive for Panther Books, who issued the paperback edition in 1977 under the title *Dark Secrets*. Certainly this set-in-the-near-future story of a group of wealthy degenerates and their parasites seeking to blow their minds, and other parts of each other, in a weekend of drug-stimulated, alcoholic, polymorphously perverse sex 'n' violence, was less entertainingly funny than its predecessor. The humour was sicker, the Swiftian misanthropy more marked, and the narrator of the novel urged his mostly loathsome cast of characters towards their final catastrophe with almost hysterical glee. What, readers might have been forgiven for wondering, had Providence done to the youthful literary editor of the *New Statesman* that he should rise up in WC1 and shake his fist at creation with such *saeva indignatio*?

The picture of modern life in Martin Amis's new novel* is hardly less bleak, but the bleakness is more obviously motivated in narrative and psychological terms; and although there is plenty in it to make the unprepared reader blush or blench, it will strike those who come to it from *Dead Babies* as a comparatively restrained, compassionate, even sentimental novel. It is certainly more disciplined, more shapely than its predecessors, though the gain in control seems to have been paid for with a certain loss of rhetorical verve. *Success* consists, formally, of two interweaving and overlapping monologues emanating from two young men, Terence Service and his foster-brother Gregory Riding. To adopt the simple class terminology of the novel, Terry was born a yob, but adopted in childhood by the posh Ridings when his father, already suspected of murdering Terry's mother, was convicted of murdering his younger sister. Gregory also has a younger sister, Ursula, and the two boys were born within a day of each other: it is a novel of symmetries. At the time of the principal action, Terry and Gregory are sharing a small flat in Bayswater, and Gregory seems to be enjoying all the success. That is to say, Gregory claims to be successful, and Terry envies him and feels himself to be a failure; and since the reader has no other sources of information there is nothing, except perhaps the suspicious overripeness of Gregory's prose style, to make him doubt the accuracy of the picture. Bisexual Gregory goes off nightly to expensive orgies and is merely bored by the nubile young women begging to be bedded by him;

* M. Amis, *Success* (Jonathan Cape, 1978).

while Terry, at the time the novel opens, has been unwillingly celibate for six months. Greg is tall, handsome, and has an easy, glamorous job in a West End art gallery. Terry is shortish, fattish, with gingery hair that is falling out and teeth that are going dead. He works in an office full of men frightened by the prospect of redundancy, buying and selling things by telephone. When he sets up the office temp for seduction, Gregory unscrupulously cuts him out. Whereas Gregory's reports on his doings exude narcissistic self-satisfaction, Terry's express self-loathing, despair and fear of sinking back into the social abyss from which he was raised. Gregory seems to have modelled his prose style on Lawrence Durrell, Nabokov and Firbank (he has also evidently been reading Vonnegut – cf. his sensations on being fellated, "for a few seconds every cell in my body shakes with ravenous applause" with Vonnegut's starving POW licking a spoonful of malt syrup, "A moment went by, and then every cell in Billy's body shook him with ravenous gratitude and applause"). Terry uses a more restricted, but no less rhetorical, code:

Ursula moving in here with us has proved to be a bonus in all kinds of ways. One particularly heartening thing, of course, is that she is fucked up, clearly very fucked up indeed, much more fucked up than I am for instance, possibly (who knows?) totally fucked up for ever, decisively fucked up for good; no matter how fucked up I get, she will always be that little bit more fucked up than I am: it is a virtual certainty that I will never be able to get quite as fucked up as she is fucked up already. This is good. Ursula is, in addition, fucked up in a way radically at odds with the way in which I am fucked up. Everything observable about me is fucked up, my face is fucked up, my body is fucked up, my hair is fucked up, my cock is fucked up, my family is all fucked up. Nothing observable about Ursula, on the other hand, is in the slightest bit fucked up: looks, ability, background, advantages – all this, on the contrary, notably unfucked up. And yet Ursula, Ursula Riding, my foster sister, is *fucked up*. She is *fucked up*. This also is good.

Ursula moves in with her brothers following a suicide attempt and Terry finds in her a willing sexual partner in anything short of actual intercourse. Encouraged by this development, and by a dramatic improvement in his income due to being adopted by the union man at the office (an effective comic cameo, this character), Terry grows in self-confidence. Gregory's, meanwhile, seems to be slipping. Discrepancies appear between the two narratives which we are increasingly apt to resolve in Terry's favour. There seems to be no reason to doubt, however, Gregory's account of having had sexual relations with his sister in childhood. In an atmosphere of deepening jealousy, migraine and neurosis, Ursula offers herself again to Gregory, is spurned, and turns in desperation to Terry, who possesses her fully at last, borrowing the very language of Gregory's account to describe the deed, which is as pleasureless as ever. Ursula, apparently traumatized by this double incest, makes another, successful suicide attempt. Gregory, broken up with guilt, confesses that he has been largely lying to the reader about his glamorous, affluent, erotically fulfilled existence. Terry, toughly observing that he has lost a sister twice, shruggingly dedicates himself to his new career of being a success. There are ugly signs that it may bring out in him a capacity for violence inherited from his father.

The title of the book is, of course, ironic. It also vibrates with puns: *suck*, *sex* and *cess* all seems to lurk relevantly in its syllables. Behind the façade of a swinging, sophisticated metropolis lie madness, impotence and death. Its streets are choked by rubbish and populated by stoned, malevolent, cowed or otherwise fucked-up citizens who do not want to be what they are. ("They may not especially want to be anything else, but, boy, they don't want to be what they are" – Terry). Aeroplanes drone in the sky above, taunting the characters with the impossibility of escape. Their own characteristic mode of transport is the Tube train, "bursting from its hole in the earth like an ugly beast", preceded by "dirty winds from the earth's core". They live profoundly boring, repetitive, culturally undernourished lives. *Success* is a novel of disillusionment, and by the device of the double narrative the reader is made to enact the process of disillusionment. The two young men talk directly to the reader, address him as "you", try to discredit each other. No attempt is made to "naturalize" this convention by inventing a plausible framework for the twin confessions. Indeed, by making the two narrators occasionally use each other's words and phrases, Mr Amis calls attention to the artificiality of his form, and makes clear that its function is expressive rather than realistic. The novel's technical accomplishment does not, however, entirely disguise the fact that the chief characters, and their doomed, incestuous relationships, offer little variation on familiar stereotypes, and it is difficult, therefore, to care about them quite as much as one seems to be expected to. Engrossing to read, *Success* does not resonate in the mind once one has put it down. It leaves open the question of which direction its author's considerable talent will take in the future: spleen or sensibility?

[*Postscript:* I suppose that, eight years later, one would have to answer, "spleen"; but really the question seems inadequate to define the imaginative energies of Amis's latest, and most impressive novel, *Money* (1984).]

Structural Defects (1980)

As an academic critic and university teacher specializing in modern literature and literary theory, I spend much of my time these days reading books and articles that I can barely understand and that cause my wife (a graduate with a good honours degree in English language and literature) to utter loud cries of pain and nausea if her eyes happen to fall on them.

At the same time I am uncomfortably aware that literary criticism no longer has the prestige it once enjoyed in our culture at large. These two facts are not unconnected. The most important, trail-blazing criticism now being produced is written in a style that is impenetrable to the layman. To paraphrase Yeats, the most readable critics lack all conviction and the least are full of passionate intensity. (There are, of course, exceptions.)

What has brought this state of affairs about is something loosely called structuralism. If you know what structuralism is, and names like Jakobson, Lévi-Strauss, Barthes, Lacan, Derrida, mean anything to you, I would hazard a guess that you are in higher education on the humanities side, or not long out of it; and if you don't, and aren't, you are evidence for the point I wish to make, which is that a very unhealthy gap has opened up between educated discourse inside and outside the academy.

Structuralism marches under many different banners (some more accurately described as "post-structuralist") and has invaded more than one discipline. In film studies the approach is known as "semiotics" or "semiology", in history and sociology as "theory", and its most fashionable manifestation in literary studies at present is "deconstruction". It has had a powerful impact on linguistics, anthropology and psychoanalysis.

Its basic premise is that meaning is not in things but in the relations we establish between them, that "reality", including the human self, is not given but produced, pre-eminently through language. . . . But already I see your eyes glaze over, or twitch away to some more seductive corner of the newspaper page. It is, alas, very difficult to explain in simple language what structuralism is all about or why anyone should bother with it. And the task gets more difficult all the time.

Structuralism started as a method of explaining how the products of human culture "work" by using linguistic models. For instance, it might explain the difference between the Benson & Hedges cigarette ads and the ones for Marlboro thus: in the former the product is highlighted by a surrealistic visual metaphor – a surprising similarity is established between the product and things otherwise different (the pyramids, a flight of china ducks, etc.) – while in the latter it is associated through realistic photography with a certain way of life that is deemed enviable or admirable, suggesting that they go together like cause and effect or part and whole.

The beauty of this distinction (which corresponds to the difference between metaphor and metonymy as figures of speech) is that it will apply equally well to all cigarette ads – and to many other things as well. A few years ago I published a book applying it to different modes of modern literature. I tried to make the book as lucid and readily intelligible as I could, but outside the academic world it was received with bafflement and sometimes derision.

The exponents of post-structuralism do not even try to be lucid and intelligible. There seem to be two motives for this. The respectable reason is that these writers believe there is no single, simple "meaning" to be grasped anywhere, at any time, and the experience of reading their books is designed to teach that uncomfortable lesson. The less respectable reason is that their command of a prestigious but impenetrable jargon constitutes power – the power to intimidate their professional peers.

For structuralism has not gone unresisted by intellectuals still clinging valiantly to empiricism, humanism, "common sense". From time to time such conflicts make a small impression on the public consciousness – for example, the recent polemic by Kevin Brownlow in the *New Statesman* against film semiology, and the subsequent correspondence; but for the most part the arguments are like dogfights between supersonic jets high in the stratosphere, while the civilian population goes obliviously about its business down below.

Does this matter? I think it does. The intellectual and artistic life of a society requires a constant refreshment by new ideas, which are formulated by the intellectual avant-garde, and then permeate down through educated society by means of the media. In this process they are inevitably simplified, and perhaps vulgarized, but this is better than no ideas getting through at all, which is what seems to be happening now in this country.

At the turn of the year, the posh papers were full of retrospective articles about the 70s – its trends, fads and fashions, but nowhere did I see a mention of structuralism. BBC television will carefully explain relativity and catastrophe theory to the viewing millions, but if there has ever been a programme about structuralism, I missed it. Posy Simmonds's genial jeering at George Weber, the Polytechnic lecturer, in her witty *Guardian* cartoon strip, is about all the national press has done to record the most significant intellectual movement of our time.

It looks as if structuralism may be the first such movement to go through the complete life-cycle of innovation, orthodoxy and obsolescence, without ever touching the popular consciousness.

[*Postscript*: The concluding prophecy of this article, published in the *Observer* in the spring of 1980, was spectacularly falsified less than a year later by the "Colin MacCabe affair". The denial of tenure to a young lecturer in the English Faculty at Cambridge University, allegedly because of his post-structuralist views, caught the attention of the media; and for a few weeks it was impossible to open one of the upmarket British newspapers, or even *Newsweek*, without the word "structuralism" leaping off the page. Whether the populace were any the wiser as a result is, however, a matter for doubt.]

Bourgeois Triangles (1980)

It would not be entirely facetious to draw an analogy between the present state of British criticism and the present state of British industry – or at least between the attitudes that may be adopted towards the crises of confidence now affecting both those institutions. According to one point of view, literary criticism in this country is in dire need of reinvestment: new ideas, new methods, and a new sense of purpose are needed if we are to compete internationally. Our existing plant – whether supplied from the Cambridge critical tradition or the Oxford literary-historical one – is now obsolete and inefficient, and to survive as a critical power we must modernize, learning from new developments abroad, particularly in the Common Market. Another school of thought looks askance at these developments, and questions whether they constitute real progress or have added substantially to the sum of human happiness. It maintains that all will be well if we raise the tariff barriers against subversive foreign ideas and conscientiously buy British, cultivating the native critical tradition of humane common sense.

Tony Tanner's new book* is important not only for its intrinsic merit as a work of literary criticism (which is considerable) but also as a sign of the times, as an unequivocal gesture of commitment, by one of the leading British critics of his generation, to the first of the two positions outlined above. (I should perhaps say that it is one to which, with certain reservations, I incline myself.) Tanner, whose previous publications (mainly on American literature) elegantly blended Cambridge-style "close reading" with an American mode of speculative cultural criticism,

---

* A. Tanner, *Adultery in the Novel: Contract and Transgression* (Johns Hopkins University Press, 1979).

has comprehensively retooled, and emerges in this book as a brilliantly effective post-structuralist critic in the contemporary European mould. The questions he asks about his chosen topic, the answers he proposes, and the very diction and syntax of his critical style, show the clear impress of the fashionable *savants* of the last three decades – Lévi-Strauss, Barthes, Lacan, Foucault, Derrida, Althusser – and of *their* readings of the great trio of revolutionary nineteenth-century thinkers – Marx, Freud and Nietzsche.

Which is not to say that Tanner has made himself into a simulacrum of a Parisian critic, like some younger British aficionados of structuralism and post-structuralism. *Adultery in the Novel* does not, heaven be praised, read as if badly translated from the original French; on the contrary, Tanner's expository style marvellously manages to combine the lucidity and conversational ease which is one of the strengths of British criticism at its best, with the teasing, paradoxical, highly abstract mode of reasoning that is typical of "deconstructive" criticism.

To retool, Tony Tanner has travelled abroad, both literally and metaphorically. He tells us in his preface that the work for this book was begun during a year's stay at the Centre for the Advanced Study of the Behavioral Sciences at Stanford, and it was no doubt completed during the year Tanner subsequently spent at Johns Hopkins. These circumstances of composition are culturally significant. America has been much more receptive, much more creatively receptive, to the new currents of thought emanating from the Continent than has Britain; and in a paradoxical way the quickest intellectual route from London (or Oxbridge) to Paris has been via New York (or New Haven or Baltimore . . .). Nearly all the English translations of seminal structuralist and post-structuralist texts have been initiated in the United States. It is noteworthy that Tanner's own book is published by Johns Hopkins.

Without knowing the circumstances behind this fact, one may doubt whether any British press would have published a work of nearly four hundred pages, with copious footnotes, that consisted mainly of close commentary on three foreign novels (Rousseau's *Julie, ou la Nouvelle Héloïse*, Goethe's *Die Wahlverwandtschaften* and Flaubert's *Madame Bovary*); certainly not at its present price. There is, of course, a difference of economic muscle as well as intellectual motivation involved here: a causal, as well as an analogical connection between the state of British criticism and the state of British industry.

Tony Tanner begins his preface by saying, "This book is offered as an exercise in reading. It is not intended as a contribution to Comparative Literature . . ." But the decision to base it on a consideration of two French texts and one German was a bold and, in academic terms, political act: an implicit reproof to the insularity of British criticism which has for so long lived lazily on the rich deposits of the native literary tradition (I might as well confess that the duty of reviewing this book prompted me to read *Julie* and *Elective Affinities* for the first time), and an acknowledgment that the highest level of literary discussion is now truly international (rather than "Comparative") in character, drawing on a common corpus of primary and secondary sources that transcends the boundaries of national literatures. Tanner has not shirked the linguistic liabilities of such an undertaking: he quotes simultaneously from the original texts and from English translations, and his critical commentary is remarkable for its close engagement with verbal nuances only perceptible in the former.

I think it is fair to say that Tony Tanner has made himself into a post-structuralist without ever having been a structuralist – that is, without having (like, say, Roland Barthes) explored the semiotic-formalist approach to literature, with its focus on the *langue* rather than the *parole* of narrative. Perhaps this explains the remarkable ease with which he has changed his critical persona. Generically, *Adultery in the Novel* is not really foreign to the English critical tradition, being essentially the study of a particular literary theme illustrated by sensitive close reading of selected texts. It is the *style* of reading, the *kind* of questions being asked about the texts, and the kind of meanings being unfolded, that are distinctively "post-structuralist". Instead of taking adultery as a "fact" of social history, and seeing how it is reflected in literature (the procedure one would expect of a conventionally empirical type of thematic criticism) Tony Tanner approaches adultery as a symptom of, or clue to, tensions and contradictions within the system of society *and* the system of the novel that were not necessarily consciously present to those who operated those systems.

The first section of his book consists of an ambitious and fascinating discussion, drawing on Lévi-Strauss, Vico, De Rougemont and Lacan among others, and ranging in literary reference from Homer to John Updike, which begins with the shift of emphasis from "status" to "contract" as the basis of modern social order, and proceeds to consider how this affected such matters as the power of patriarchy, the position of woman, the significance of marriage as an institution, and the history of the novel as a literary form. Tanner argues that marriage (memorably defined by Vico as "a chaste carnal union consummated under fear of some divinity") was what guaranteed the stability and permanence of bourgeois society and the bourgeois novel. Adultery, particularly the adultery of the female partner, threatened to subvert this stability and therefore inspired fear and horror – but also, and for the same reasons, fascinated the literary imagination.

The bourgeois novel is therefore obsessively drawn to the theme of adultery, like a moth to the flame; but the more searchingly and explicitly it investigates this theme, the more it risks unfolding the arbitrariness and fragility of the whole bourgeois social order, and also of the narrative order on which the bourgeois novel itself is constructed.

The questioning of the institution of marriage proceeds *pari passu* with the questioning of the conventions of the classic realist text, a process apparent in the development of Henry James's work from, say, *The Portrait of a Lady* to *The Golden Bowl*. By the time we get to Lawrence and Joyce, the actual fact of adultery has lost its potency as a violation of fundamental law, and becomes marginal to other concerns, "physicality" in *Lady Chatterley's Lover*, or "linguisticity" in *Ulysses*:

> If society depends for its existence on certain rules governing what may be combined and what should be kept separate, then adultery, by bringing the wrong things together in the wrong places (or the wrong people in the wrong beds), offers an attack on those rules, revealing them to be arbitrary rather than absolute. In this way, the adulterous woman becomes the "gap" in society that gradually extends through it . . . we can see adultery as the gap, or silence, in the bourgeois novel that finally leads to its dissolution and displacement by postsocial fictional forms involving extreme states of physicality and/or linguisticity (or Proustian solipsism). The bourgeois novel of adultery finally discovers its own impossibility, and as a result sexuality, narration, and society fall apart, never to be reintegrated in the same way – if, indeed, at all.

I am not altogether convinced by this somewhat apocalyptic synthesis of literary and social history. One might be impressed, rather, by the *durability* of adultery as a theme for fiction, persisting in spite of all the changes of literary and moral fashion over the past hundred years. Tanner's discounting of the significance of adultery in Lawrence and Joyce seems to me tendentious, and his description of Updike's *Couples*, as being "as little about passion as it is about marriage; the adulteries are merely formal and technical. Adultery, we may say, no longer signifies", simply wrong. It is not a matter of indifference that Connie Chatterley and Mellors are married to other partners when he initiates her into the mysteries of sex, and Bloom's cuckoldry is no less keenly felt because he condones and in a sense connives at Molly's assignation with Boylan. There is a great deal of passion, and a great deal of guilt in *Couples*, which derive from the fact that the affairs it describes are adulterous, not mere promiscuous fornication.

But it would not be appropriate to pursue this point further, since Tony Tanner promises to deal thoroughly with the later history of his subject in a second volume. In the present one he is concerned with three novels of the high bourgeois era, of which it is true to say that the importance of adultery as an act is in inverse ratio to the explicitness of its representation in the text. Indeed, in two of them adultery does not take place at all, either in the *fabula* or the *sjuzet*. This, no doubt, is what makes them apt subjects for deconstructive criticism, which aims to make the gaps and absences of a text speak as eloquently as what is verbally present.

Of the three, Rousseau's *Julie, or the New Eloise* lends itself most simply and "innocently" to a deconstructive reading. It is a highly artificial epistolary novel of sentiment which exerted an extraordinary (and to us, today, almost incomprehensible) spell over the literary imagination of Europe from the time of its publication in 1761 to at least the second generation of English Romantic poets (Byron and Shelley, it is worth recalling, spent a week in the summer of 1816 visiting the sites of the novel around Lake Geneva in a spirit of enthusiastic homage). Ostensibly it is a story of an exceptionally passionate but sublime love (rivalling the legendary love of Eloise and Abelard) between Julie and her tutor, the poor but noble-spirited commoner who is quite unaccept-able to Julie's rank-conscious father as a suitor for her hand.

This is a very venerable narrative kernel, and in earlier literature would have been developed and resolved in one of two ways: by making the young man become eligible or showing that he was really eligible all the time (the mode of comedy and romance); or by the union-in-death of the two lovers (the mode of tragedy). Rousseau, however, deviates from these well-trodden paths by a series of developments and reversals which postpone the ultimate answer to the basic narrative question (will the lovers unite?) for several hundred pages, giving all concerned ample opportunity to describe and exhibit a wide range of intense and highly creditable feelings.

It was an essential feature of the sentimental novel not only that its characters were highly susceptible to feeling, but that these were *good* feelings. What happens is that, with the exception of Julie's father, who remains adamantly fixed in his prejudices, all the other characters act with extraordinary and unpredictable magnanimity which, so far from making moral choice easier for the others, makes it exquisitely more difficult. Thus the English Lord Bomston, at first himself attracted to Julie, immediately renounces his suit on discovering her prior attach-ment to St Preux, and goes so far as to offer to set up the lovers with an estate in England if they were to elope with each other. When Julie appeals to her beloved cousin Claire for advice, the latter, who blames herself for the fact that Julie has already surrendered her "honour" to St Preux, vows that if Julie goes to England she (Claire) will go with her, thus destroying her own life and prospects. Julie ultimately succumbs to this and other moral pressures, tells St Preux they must part, and marries the man chosen by her father, the middle-aged Monsieur de Wolmar. But de Wolmar, so far from being the odious, jealous older husband familiar from folk tale and romance, turns out to be a humane, enlightened, sensitive rationalist, who invites St Preux into his house and tries to help the former lovers live together in a state of platonic amity. In an abrupt narrative climax Julie dies, as the result of saving her own child from drowning, in an odour of sentimental sanctity, clearly hinting to St Preux that this is for the best since they would not have been able to keep their love platonic indefinitely.

What Tony Tanner's reading demonstrates, utterly convincingly, is that Julie's most intense emotional relationship is not with St Preux at all, but with the character who looks, superficially, to be the most stereotyped in the story – her father; that the most passionate scenes in the novel feature not St Preux (an essentially impotent figure, for whom writing is an onanistic substitute for sex) but Julie's father, who in a spasm of rage brutally assaults her, and then takes her on his knee and caresses her; that the ménage which Julie dreams of constructing in the latter half of the book, comprising not only her husband (who is a benign version of her father) and her lover, but also her cousin Claire, with whom she seems to have a latent lesbian relationship, and whom she plans to marry to St Preux, "involves an abandoning of distinctions, a loss of sense of difference, which could be seen to point back to that 'infamous promiscuity of things and women' that for Vico was the abhorrent state from which civilization had to emerge". The deep appeal of Rousseau's novel for its age was, presumably, that it allowed its readers to peep into this abyss under cover of the most high-minded sentiments, affording a thrilling, frightening glimpse of the polymorphous perversity of feeling that might be enjoyed if the power of the father could be overthrown, but pulling back from final abandonment to it. (That final abandonment was to come in the work of the Marquis de Sade, whose *Juliette*, as Tanner remarks, was a kind of demonic parody of *Julie*.)

There are many resemblances between *Julie* and Goethe's *Elective Affinities*, as Tanner ably demonstrates. Both novels, for instance, use the same symbolic topography divided into three zones – a house in which sex is ordered and controlled, an artificial pastoral region in which a certain amount of sexual experiment is licensed, and a wilderness or watery waste which is associated with the total surrender to passion. In both, water and boating figure prominently in connection with the pleasures and fatal perils of illicit sexuality. But these are archetypal features of the adultery story from Tristan and Iseult to *The Ambassadors*. A more striking resemblance is the way Goethe, like Rousseau, allows his characters to flirt with the idea of adultery, but not actually commit it. In the key scene of *Elective Affinities*, husband and wife sexually embrace while thinking of the two other people with whom they are respectively in love, and conceive a child who resembles the absent loved ones. The whole novel is remarkable for its displacement of erotic energy into dreaming, wishing, talking, play-acting; and it is in this feature that Tony Tanner centres his interpretation. In the presented lives of the characters he finds, "an excess of metaphor over experience":

> Images from chemistry, art, evolution, topography, fill up the void of time created by idleness; and since the characters do not set them to work, they set the characters to work.

This seems to me a fair judgment, though whether it is one that Tanner "discovered" in the gaps and silences of the text, or one that Goethe consciously inscribed into it, is not entirely clear to me. I can only offer the suggestion, for Tanner's second volume, that *Elective Affinities* may have been a source of inspiration for Ford Madox Ford's *The Good Soldier* (the central male figure of each is a mature man called Edward infatuated by a young ward, with tragic consequences for all concerned).

About *Madame Bovary*, and Tanner's reading of it, there need be less hesitation. A deconstructive reading of Flaubert's masterpiece is merely an attentive one, for he anticipated all our modern critical sophistication, ingenuity and love of paradox. He undid the classic realist text from within before it was ever named or analysed. Which is not in any way to diminish the critic's achievement. On the contrary, Tanner's long chapter on this novel is one of the finest pieces of critical explication I have read for a long time, and there are moments when, if it were performed instead of written, one would feel like bursting into applause.

Unlike the protagonists of Rousseau's and Goethe's fictions, Emma Bovary actually commits adultery – with, as we say, a vengeance; but what she discovers is that adultery is as banal and meaningless as marriage. The exciting, frightening abyss of undifferentiated and unhallowed passions, feelings and sensations into which Rousseau's and Goethe's characters peered turns out to be not so much an abyss as a void, and Flaubert's novel, apparently a scrupulously realistic rendering of a concrete, recognizable social world, is in fact a web of motifs woven out of negation, contradiction and emptiness. Let us trace just a few strands of this web, with Tanner's assistance, starting with the tax-collector, M. Binet, one of the paralysingly boring people who surround Emma.

M. Binet's hobby is making useless wooden objects with his lathe, especially countless napkin rings, for which he has no actual use, since he does not eat at home. "A napkin ring," Tanner observes, "is a material encirclement of nothing . . . it is a manufactured hole. In this we may say that it represents the *symbolic* opposite of a wedding ring . . . as a nonsymbolic *object*, however, the wedding ring is isomorphically identical to the napkin ring." The monotonous drone (*le renflement monotone*) of Binet's lathe is one of the pervasive sounds in the Bovary's village, and *renflement*, as Tanner notes, can mean snoring, of which there is a great deal in the book. "Snoring we may call the unspeech of nonconsciousness, a drowning of semantic utterances in involuntary bodily noise."

When Emma contemplates suicide by defenestration after receiving Rodolphe's letter of rejection, the lathe seems to be encouraging her: "She had only to give way, to let herself go . . . And all the time the lathe went on whirring, whirring, like a voice furiously calling her." When Emma's first lover, Léon, complains to Binet of ennui, Binet advises him to get a lathe: " '*Moi, à votre place, j'aurais un tour!*' " *Tour* can mean a "turn" as well as a lathe:

> It is one aspect of Emma Bovary that she is forever "turning", seeking continual change, but the more she turns the more she finds she is more deeply immersed in sameness. When we read that "Emma had rediscovered in adultery all the banality of marriage" we know that she is near to realizing the fatal futility of all her "turnings".

The word *tour* is very similar in sound and shape, to the word *trou*, hole, which is what Binet makes in the form of napkin rings:

> From *trou* to *tour* requires the most minimal lexical displacement, which first of all may seem to change a great deal (the hole *transformed* into a lathe) but then has the opposite effect of decreasing our sense of distinction (there is no *difference* between the hole and the lathe). Just so, Emma thinks that the displacement of adultery will transform her life, and discovers that it changes nothing.

Binet's lathe is worked by a wheel or *roue*, and the French word echoes not only *tour* and *trou*, but also Emma's maiden name Rouault, and the name of the city of Rouen, in which she abandons herself most completely to adultery, notably inside the famous closed carriage which wheels around the streets of Rouen in apparently aimless circles to the astonishment of all observers.

These snippets must suffice to indicate the subtlety and penetration of Tony Tanner's critical commentary. They may also suggest what a full reading of the chapter on *Madame Bovary* strongly impressed upon the present reviewer: that the richness of the commentary gradually overwhelms the original thesis of the book, and cannot in the end be contained within it. Tanner's delicate and precise unfolding of all the manifold and intricate correspondences, leitmotifs, symmetries and inversions, at every level of the text from the phoneme to the narrative sequence, does not in the end convince one that there is some kind of homology between the system of bourgeois marriage and the system of the bourgeois novel. But it *does* demonstrate, very amply and beautifully, the truth of a much more abstract and universal principle, classically formulated by the *doyen* of structuralism, Roman Jakobson: "The poetic function projects the principle of equivalence from the axis of selection into the axis of combination." When the ideological heat generated by "deconstruction" has died down, we may well decide that its most valuable contribution was in stretching and enhancing our understanding of how this fundamental principle, the $E=mc^2$ of modern poetics, actually operates in literary texts. *Adultery in the Novel* will be a major piece of evidence for such a conclusion.

What There Is To Tell (1980)

For most of his professional life, Graham Greene might have been described as the Greta Garbo of modern English letters. He preferred to be alone. A wartime Penguin edition of *England Made Me* in my possession records on the back cover that "he . . . has always lived a quiet life and shunned literary circles." Widely regarded as, in Hugh Walpole's words (quoted on the same cover), "the finest English novelist of his generation", he avoided the public exposure that usually accompanies such exalted cultural status. He seldom gave interviews to journalists, and was, indeed, seldom to be found by them. He travelled widely and eventually settled in France. On the rare occasions when he agreed to discuss his work on television, he would allow his voice to be heard, but not his face to be seen. His behaviour, in short, manifested an almost fanatical desire to protect his privacy and to preserve his "cover", like one of his own fictitious secret agents, as he moved restlessly about the globe.

In recent years, however, Mr Greene has somewhat relaxed his reserve and allowed his public to see something of the man behind the work. He has given a good many interviews, and in 1971 published a volume of autobiography about his early years, *A Sort of Life*. Over the last decade or so he has been reissuing his books in a collected edition, each with a short introduction describing the sources, background and circumstances of composition of the text in question. He has now woven these introductions together, with some pieces of occasional journalism and personal diaries, to form a sequel to *A Sort of Life*.*

It would be wrong to suppose that Mr Greene has quite abandoned his previous reticence. The many interviews he has given are somewhat

*G. Greene, *Ways of Escape* (Bodley Head, 1980).

repetitive, as though he is keeping to a carefully prepared and memorized script, and one sometimes suspects that he is playing a private game with the media – giving their representatives the illusion of getting new facts, which on sober inspection prove to be already well known or nugatory. *A Sort of Life* was a very discreet, selective memoir, and *Ways of Escape* is still more so. Greene gives his reasons in the Preface to the new book:

> When I wrote a fragment of autobiography under the title *A Sort of Life* I closed the record at the age of about twenty-seven. I felt then that the future years belonged as much to others as to myself. I couldn't infringe *their* copyright . . . They had a right to privacy, and it was impossible to deal with my private life without involving theirs. All the same I had tasted the pleasure – often enough a sad pleasure – of remembering, and so I began a series of introductions to the Collected Edition of my books, looking back on the circumstances in which the books were conceived and written. They too were after all "a sort of life".

The tendency to look back contemplatively on one's life as one gets nearer the end of it (Greene is seventy-six this year, though you would never guess it from his appearance or his recent books) is a natural human instinct, and the obligation to protect the privacy of others is an honourable motive for reticence. But it is doubtful whether these are the only factors involved here. Greene's teasing, almost coquettish play with the public's intense curiosity about his private life and personal character centres on a profound paradox at the heart of writing itself – or, rather, on a set of interrelated paradoxes. Are books made out of life, or out of other books? Does the writer write his novel, or does the novel "write" the writer? Is the "implied author" of a novel – the creative mind to whom we attribute the text and whom we praise or blame for its successes and failures – the "same" as the "real author", the actual historical individual who produced the text, but has a life outside it? Does a novel convince because it is "true to life", or because it produces a rhetorical "reality-effect"? Are novels based upon real people and events, or is that reality itself a human construct, another fiction? Dogmatic formalists or structuralists will give one set of answers to these questions, orthodox literary historians and biographers another, but the honest answers are paradoxical, even contradictory: "yes and no", "both are true".

Graham Greene has never manifested much interest in the abstract questions of literary theory that occupy academic critics, but these paradoxes and contradictions permeate his reflections on his own writing. One might cite his equivocal attitude to the phrase "Greeneland", so often used by critics to characterize his evocation of place:

Some critics have referred to a strange violent "seedy" region of the mind (why did I ever popularize that last adjective?) which they call Greeneland, and I have sometimes wondered whether they go round the world blinkered. "This is Indo-China," I want to exclaim, "this is Mexico, this is Sierra Leone, carefully and accurately described. I have been a newspaper correspondent as well as a novelist. I assure you that the dead child lay in the ditch in just that attitude. In the canal of Phat Diem the bodies stuck out of the water . . ." But I know that argument is useless. They won't believe the world they haven't noticed is like that.

A later reference is not quite so emphatically positivistic:

To cheer ourselves [in West Africa] we used to hunt cockroaches by the light of electric torches, marking in pencil on the walls one point for a certain death, half a point if the roach had been washed down the lavatory bowl. I described this pursuit in *The Heart of the Matter*. Greeneland perhaps. I can only say it is the land where I have passed much of my life.

In describing Santiago, Cuba, under Batista's regime, the note of protest returns:

Nobody came to Santiago now, except presumably the spies against whom I had been warned. The night was hot and humid; it was nearly the hour of the unofficial curfew, and the hotel clerk made no pretence of welcoming strangers. The taxis soon packed up and went, the square cleared of people, a squad of soldiers went by, a man in a dirty white drill suit rocked himself backwards and forwards in a chair in the hall, making a small draught in the mosquitoey evening. I was reminded of Villahermosa during the persecution in Tabasco. The smell of a police station lay over the city. I was back in what my critics imagine to be Greeneland.

The writer's objection to the term "Greeneland" seems to be based on a feeling that it impugns the veracity of his account of the world, yet Greene himself is well aware of how writing modifies the "facts" it sets out to describe. He demonstrates the point himself in a fascinating comparison of three different versions of the same episode (a bad attack of fever which he suffered on his Liberian safari): his own bald diary entry for the day, his later writing up of the incident in *Journey Without Maps*, and the independently-written account of his cousin Barbara, who accompanied him on the trip. There is much more in common between the two "literary" texts than between either of them and the original diary. As Greene says: "'I' the diarist and 'I' the writer were distinct persons."

It is not just a matter of what the writer puts in: it is also a matter of what he leaves out. (Barbara Greene herself was almost entirely left out of *Journey Without Maps*, which greatly heightened the sense of the narrator's isolation from Western civilization, and made his journey appear more of an exploration of his own self.) We may accept that the details of Phat Diem or Santiago were observable by anyone who happened to be there, but venture to think that only one writer would have selected *them* and not others present in the scene, and described them in those words in that particular order.

In fact, Graham Greene's impatient dismissal of the Greeneland tag has as much to do with his suspicion of criticism as with his claims to authenticity. And here we encounter another paradox at the heart of writing – not peculiar to Greene, but very keenly felt and expressed by him. On the one hand, the author wishes to be read carefully and sympathetically, to have his intentions understood and his technical choices recognized. Greene is sharp, on occasion, with critics who have offended in these respects – complaining, for instance, of the critic who, failing to understand the nuances of "point of view", supposed that because Anthony and Kate in *England Made Me* did not recognize the incestuous nature of their bond, their creator was equally unaware of it. He also corrects the reviewer who read strained religious symbolism into the names Harry Lime and Holly Martins in *The Third Man*, connecting "Lime" with a passage in *The Golden Bough* and "Holly" with Christmas.

> The truth of the matter is, I wanted for my "villain" a name natural and yet disagreeable, and to me "Lime" represented the quicklime in which murderers were said to be buried. An association of ideas, not, as the reviewer claimed, a symbol. As for Holly, it was because my first choice of name, Rollo, had not met with the approval of Joseph Cotten [the actor who played the role, and thought the original name had homosexual overtones]. So much for symbols.

Yet there is a sense in which the writer fears the perceptive critic even more than he despises the bad one, for the former threatens to rob the creative process of its mystery and excitement, making the literary text seem a determined rather than a free act, a confirmation of the critic's diagnosis rather than the artist's hard-won discovery of what it was he wanted to say. There comes a time when the established author "is more afraid to read his favourable critics than his unfavourable, for with terrible patience they unroll before his eyes the unchanging pattern of the carpet. If he has depended a great deal on his unconscious, on his ability to forget even his own books when they are once on the public shelves, his critics remind him – this theme originated ten years ago, that simile which came so unthinkingly to his pen a few weeks back was used nearly twenty years ago in a passage where . . ."

Several passages in this book make it clear that writing has never come easily to Greene. *A Confidential Agent* was written in six weeks on benzedrine, but usually the composition of a novel is for him hard and protracted labour over years rather than weeks, subject to deep depressions, blocks, self-doubt and boredom. What makes it all worthwhile is precisely the thrill of the unexpected and unpredictable development in the story: the strokes of luck, or grace, that solve apparently intractable problems or make the work in progress better than one ever dared to hope. Greene attributes these blessings to the operation of the writer's unconscious, since they often manifest themselves to him after sleep and dream. But this account of the creative process does, of course, to some extent undermine his occasional attempts to control and limit the meanings of his fiction by reference to his conscious intentions. Perhaps the critic who saw an allusion to Frazer in *The Third Man* was guilty of what I. A. Richards called mnemonic irrelevance, but the arboreal and social connotations of the pair Holly/Lime cannot simply be brushed aside. Symbolism can use the novelist as much as the novelist uses symbolism.

The writer tends to feel just as equivocal about lay readers as about professional critics. Naturally he wants to have readers, but he is generally reluctant to meet them, since the gap between the "real" and the "implied" author tends to become an embarrassment in such encounters. Graham Greene has suffered particularly from his Catholic admirers in this respect. *The Power and the Glory, The Heart of the Matter* and *The End of the Affair* were novels of very powerful religious sentiment of a distinctively Catholic kind – much concerned with casuistry, eschatology, the miraculous and the mystical – and they were also the novels which established Greene internationally as a novelist of the first rank. In consequence, he came to be regarded as a kind of lay theologian and potential confessor by troubled and eccentric Catholic readers all over the world – like the French priest who "popped up unannounced and inopportunely one evening in Anacapri, as I was catching the bus to Capri with my mistress, trailing a smoke of dust from his long black soutane".

Twenty or thirty years ago, that casual allusion to a mistress would have sent shock waves of scandal rippling through the Catholic world. The Church Greene joined in 1928 liked to have distinguished authors in its flock – they were good for the Church's image among the intelligentsia – but only if they toed the orthodox line on matters of faith and morals. The Holy Office condemned *The Power and the Glory* as heretical, and after reading *The End of the Affair* Pope Pius XII told Cardinal Heenan: "I think this man is in trouble. If he ever comes to you, you must help him." Greene, a convert in adulthood, had never acquired that automatic deference to clerical authority or the acceptance of sexual repression that were characteristic of British "ghetto"

Catholicism. No wonder he resisted and resented the label "Catholic novelist" so often pinned upon him, and preached the writer's duty to be "disloyal" to institutions. His style of Catholicism has become increasingly agnostic as the years have passed, but in the pluralist climate of the post-Conciliar Church it does not excite as much comment as formerly. His friend Evelyn Waugh, a much more orthodox and "loyal" Catholic, was dismayed by *A Burnt-Out Case* when it appeared in 1961. "I don't think you can blame people who read the book as a recantation of faith," Waugh wrote to Greene at the time, and alluded sadly to Browning's "The Lost Leader".

> I felt the discussion was becoming too serious. Evelyn's reference to the Lost Leader had surprised me and even shocked me a little, for had I not always regarded him as *my* leader? To bring the correspondence to a close I sent him a flippant postcard – I think one of Brighton pier – "My love to Milton, Burns, Shelley and warn them that Spender and Day Lewis are on the way. I shall be grateful for all your coppers. A voice from the Rear and the Slaves," to which he replied in kind, "Mud in your mild and magnificent eye. Hoping for a glad and confident morning." The cloud had passed. Browning had served us both well.

(Readers who did not grow up with Palgrave's *Golden Treasury* will need to look up the text to get the full flavour of this correspondence.)

Graham Greene's books usually have a thematic keyword which keeps recurring – "pity" in *The Heart of the Matter*, "trust" in *A Confidential Agent*, "love and hate" in *The End of the Affair*, "failure" in *A Sort of Life*. There is no difficulty about identifying it in the new book. "Escape again, I suspect that the word will chime from the title page on throughout this book," he writes, on page 13, recalling the plot of an early, unpublished novel. The suffocating embrace of Mother Church was only one of the things Graham Greene found it necessary to escape from; others included bourgeois respectability, boredom, depression, the mass media, the literary world, his fans. In one sense, *Ways of Escape* belongs with his travel books, since much of it is a record of journeys to distant places in Africa, Central and South America, South-East Asia, the Middle East. He must surely have logged more flying hours than any writer of his stature in the world. He has been often in situations of extreme danger and extreme discomfort – in Vietnam, in the Malayan jungle, in Duvalier's nightmare Haiti, in the London Blitz – and he writes vividly yet unpretentiously about these experiences. Even a reader unacquainted with Graham Greene's fiction would enjoy this book thoroughly. To anyone who knows the novels well it is utterly fascinating. And part of the fascination is our awareness that the author has not told all that there is to tell, or anything like it.

From a View to a Death (1980)

What the American short-story writer Leonard Michaels calls "the condemned prisoner story" (in a book, *I Would Have Saved Them If I Could*, which contains and alludes to several examples of the genre) has exercised a powerful fascination over the modern literary imagination. This is not surprising. Capital punishment, and the ritual associated with it, dramatize the inevitability and finality of personal death with a stark intensity that no other action, not even terminal illness, can match. We all know that we must die, but most of the time we suppress the knowledge, or others suppress it for us; only the condemned prisoner must live with the certain knowledge of the exact day and hour at which he will pass from life to death. And, since capital punishment is a legal institution, an act through which the State asserts the sanctity of human life by taking one, it brings into consciousness the paradoxes and contradictions on which civilization is founded, and poses in an extreme and daunting way the perennial problems of evil, responsibility and justice.

Among literary polemics against capital punishment, Orwell's "A Hanging" is a classic of the documentary prose method, Oscar Wilde's "The Ballad of Reading Gaol" of the poetic. More existential in emphasis are the celebrated fabulations of Ambrose Bierce ("Occurrence at Owl Creek Bridge") and Borges ("The Secret Miracle") which stretch the instant before death to encompass an epic of desire. In the nineteenth-century novel (putting aside such cases as *The Heart of Midlothian* and *Adam Bede*, in which the machinery of the plot allows the prisoner – and thus, vicariously, the reader – a reprieve) one thinks particularly of Dickens's fascination with the subject: his gloating account of Fagin in the condemned cell, Wemmick's disconcertingly casual interview with the "Colonel" in *Great Expectations*, and the grimly ironic reversal by which the monstrous hangman Dennis in *Barnaby Rudge* meets his end. Dickens was opposed to capital punishment in principle, but was drawn irresistibly to witness, and to describe, several executions. Byron described the guillotining of three men in a letter which gave Leonard Michaels his title:

> The first turned me quite hot and thirsty, and made me shake so that I could hardly hold the opera glass. (I was close, but was determined to see, as one should see everything once, with attention); the second and third (which shows how dreadfully soon things grow indifferent) had no effect on me as a horror, though I would have saved them if I could.

One could go back at least as far as *Measure for Measure* (before the Renaissance, the condemned prisoner is usually a martyr, and the meaning of his story quite different). But while reading Norman Mailer's monumental and enthralling non-fiction novel about the execution of Gary Gilmore,* the literary parallel which came most readily to my mind was James Boswell's account of his dealings with his client John Reid, in that volume of the Journals entitled *Boswell for the Defence* in the Yale edition. Reid, whom Boswell had succeeded in getting acquitted of a charge of sheep-stealing in his first court case, was in 1774 again charged with the same offence (then a capital one) and in spite of Boswell's eloquent defence, was found guilty and sentenced to death. Boswell, who believed the man was really guilty, urged him to confess before he died, but Reid staunchly asserted his innocence. While seeking, without much hope, to obtain a commutation of the sentence to transportation, Boswell visited his client frequently in the condemned cell, and became obsessed with the case to an extent which alarmed his wife and friends. He was deeply impressed by the calm resignation with which Reid contemplated his imminent death and the steadfastness with which he averred his innocence, but he was unable to reconcile these two facts with each other, or with his professional intuition that Reid was guilty. Although Boswell's interest was sincerely compassionate, it always hovered on the edge of the purely aesthetic: "I was desirous to have his picture done *while under sentence of death* and was therefore rather desirous that, in case a respite were to come, it should not come till he had sat his full time . . . When it was finished, and hung upon a nail to dry, it swung, which looked ominous to my fancy."

The respite, or stay of execution, does come, but upsets rather than encourages Reid, who however persists in maintaining his innocence. Boswell concocts a crazy plot to rush Reid's body from the scaffold and attempt to resuscitate him. He resolves "to know the truth by being with

---

* N. Mailer, *The Executioner's Song* (Hutchinson, 1980).

him to the very last minute of his life". At their final interview, with the executioner waiting to escort Reid to the scaffold, the latter again avers his innocence. "Then," says Boswell, "I shall trouble you no more upon this head. I believe you. God forbid that I should not believe a fellow man in your situation." Just before he is turned off Reid speaks from the scaffold: "Take warning: mine is an unjust sentence." But some of the people around think he said: "Mine is a just sentence." The hangman confirms the former version, but a tantalizing, irresolvable doubt lingers to haunt Boswell.

Gary Gilmore believed he had been hanged in eighteenth-century England in a previous incarnation, but that is not what invites a comparison between Mailer's and Boswell's versions of the condemned prisoner story; rather, it is that both Reid and Gilmore, in their different ways, by taking up an unexpected stance towards their own imminent executions, fascinated and puzzled and provoked those who observed them to the point of obsession. Both stories are as much about the observers as about the observed.

As everyone must know by now, Gary Gilmore committed two callous murders in Utah in 1976, was charged and convicted and sentenced to death, but refused to exercise the right of appeal which would have ensured either the commutation of his sentence to life imprisonment or the indefinite postponement of his execution. By refusing to play the part expected of him, by insisting upon being executed, Gilmore called the State's bluff. American society was no longer able to hide its uncertainty about what to do with proven killers behind the interminable delays and technical quibbling of the legal process. "I believe I was given a fair trial and I think the sentence is just and I am willing to accept it like a man," said Gilmore. "Don't the people of Utah have the courage of their convictions?" This was Gilmore's mock, and it was quite unanswerable except on Gilmore's own terms. The officials and lawyers of the Utah Attorney General's office accordingly put in motion the machinery for carrying out the sentence, but it made them feel uneasy, and a little foolish, that they were collaborating with Gilmore rather than punishing him, while at the same time they were taking a great deal of flak from the American Civil Liberties Union and the National Association for the Advancement of Colored People. These liberal pressure groups tried every legal device to stop Gilmore's execution because they feared it would jeopardize the lives of all the other men on Death Rows across America. Gilmore had a mock for them too.

V. Jinks Dabney of ACLU, what a phoney-sounding name. You said in *Salt Lake Tribune* there is still a chance that Gilmore may flip-flop and change his mind about wanting to be executed. No chance,

V. Jinks Dabney, no way, never. You and ACLU are the flip-flops. You take one stand on abortion, which is actually execution. You are all for that. And then you take another stand on capital punishment. You're against that. Where are your convictions, V. Jinks Dabney? Do you and ACLU know where you really stand on anything?

Remarks like that, taken from one of many tape-recorded conversations between Gilmore and his lawyers in the maximum-security wing of Utah State Prison, inevitably make one wonder how and why a man capable of such wit and acumen came to be in the condemned cell at all. Gary Gilmore was a gifted artist, had an IQ of 140 and could quote Shelley (when *Newsweek* attributed the poem to him, he enjoyed the joke). But at thirty-six he had spent eighteen of his last twenty-two years in gaol, and since being sent to reform school he had never been free for longer than eight months at a stretch. He described himself mockingly as "the eternal recidivist". His crimes of robbery with violence were invariably rash, impulsive and unprofitable. He came to Utah on parole, generously sponsored by his cousin Brenda. This woman, her relatives and friends, did as much as anyone could expect, and more, to assist Gary's rehabilitation.

They lent him money and clothing, found him a job, helped him buy an old car, tolerated his rough manners. But Gary was impatient: he wanted more money, a better car. He commenced a passionate affair with a young girl of nineteen, Nicole Barrett, already twice married and with two children, a beautiful but unhappy young woman whose psychological and sexual history was almost as self-destructive as Gary's own. When Gary got frustrated, over money or sex, he drank, and when he drank he got dangerous. Estranged from Nicole, and pressed for money to make the payments on his new pick-up truck, he went on a rampage and in one twenty-four-hour period robbed the tills of a filling station and a motel office, shooting their respective attendants through the head at point-blank range. He never counted his loot and when he was told, shortly after his arrest, that it scarcely amounted to $250 in all, he wept and said, "I hope they execute me for it. I ought to die for what I did."

Who could gainsay him? For a few paltry dollars, and the relief of frustration, he had laid waste the lives of two fine, decent young men, and the lives of their wives and families. The disproportion between motive and deed baffled everyone. Lawyers, police, psychiatrists, and journalists again and again probed for some secret clue to the enigma – some concealed fact, some childhood trauma, some sexual hang-up; and again and again Gary gave them the same answer, but most explicitly in his last interview, a telephone conversation on the very eve of his execution: "I was always capable of murder . . . I can become totally devoid of feelings for others, unemotional." The uncomfortable idea that Gilmore compels us to contemplate is that there may be such a thing as innate evil, which can be neither explained nor expelled by conditioning. "Are you the devil?" Nicole once asked him, on an impulse, early in their relationship. He wasn't, but, as he said to her later in a remarkable letter written from prison, "I might be further from God than I am from the devil. Which is not a good thing . . . It seems that I know evil more intimately than I know goodness and that's not a good thing either. I want to get even, to be made even, whole, my debts paid (whatever it may take!) to have no blemish, no reason to feel guilt or fear . . ." If Gilmore thought he could best achieve this by accepting his sentence, who could gainsay him? His comment on the alternative was shrewd and all too plausible: "What do I do, rot in prison? growing old and bitter and eventually work this round in my mind to where it reads that I'm the one who's getting fucked around, that I'm just an innocent victim of society's bullshit?"

In an afterword, Norman Mailer describes *The Executioner's Song* as a true-life story told as a novel. This means more than selecting and ordering the narration of events with an eye to effects of suspense and ironic juxtaposition; and it means more than evoking atmosphere, setting and character by an artful selection of synecdochic details; it means above all presenting events as they were perceived and reflected upon by the people involved, rather than from the detached perspective of a historian. Norman Mailer has written non-fiction novels before – *The Armies of the Night, Miami and the Siege of Chicago* – but in those books he himself appeared, in the third person, as the dominant character. *The Executioner's Song* is remarkable, among Mailer's works, for the almost complete absence of the author's personality from the text. Not only does Mailer himself not appear in the story, he seldom makes his presence felt stylistically. Following the model of Truman Capote's *In Cold Blood* (1966), a book on a very similar subject for which the author coined the term "non-fiction novel", but going even further in stylistic self-effacement, Mailer tells his story very largely within the constraints of the linguistic registers of the people involved. He makes extensive use of the rhetorical device known to stylisticians as "free indirect speech", in which the narrator omits those tags, "he said", "she perceived", etc., that overtly signal his presence in the text, and describes the characters' perceptions and reflections in their own kind of language – e.g. this passage from Nicole's point of view:

Gary came home in a sloppy old windcheater with the sleeves cut off. His pants were a mess, and he was half drunk. He told her to go over with him to Val Conlin's to examine the truck. She asked him to get cleaned up first. She didn't really want to be seen with him. He looked like he slept out in the yard.

Gilmore himself, it should be noted, is never represented in this way, as a reflector of events; he is always an object of other people's perception, and when his actions are described by the narrator, it is without any psychological interiority. The challenging enigma of his character is thus preserved, and respected, to the end. Readers, like the people associated with him, have to judge Gilmore for themselves, on the evidence of his words and deeds. An additional reason for this strategy, and for Mailer's self-effacement, was no doubt the fact that Mailer himself never met Gilmore. By the time Mailer started researching the book, Gilmore was no longer available for interview.

Although Gary Gilmore is never presented from within, he dominates the first half of the book, which is called "Western Voices": the focus is upon his character, his impact on the dull, decent society of small-town Utah, the cruel folly of his crimes, and the formation of his existential decision to die. In Part 2, "Eastern Voices" (the titles of the parts indicate the book's narrative method), the emphasis shifts somewhat from Gary to the people who surround him: guarding him, observing him, trying to get him reprieved, trying to get him executed, trying to understand him and, especially, trying to report him. The media men move into Utah in a big way, among them one Larry Schiller, a successful photographer turned agent-producer, who is sensitive about his reputation as a practitioner of morbid and unscrupulous cheque-book journalism, but determined to secure the rights to what he identifies as a story of extraordinary human interest.

Shortly after Schiller's arrival on the scene, Gary Gilmore's deathwish became a *Liebestod*: Nicole Barrett (who had taken to wandering round the walls of the prison yelling "I love you, Gary Gilmore", and had already tried cutting her wrists) succeeded in smuggling an overdose of Seconal tablets into the gaol in her vagina and the two lovers made a suicide pact that failed only because the dose was not quite big enough. Gilmore was getting upset by the delays to his execution, and was racked with jealousy on Nicole's account, as Schiller discovered when he got hold of Gary's letters to her from prison, an unbelievable haul of a thousand pages of confession, self-analysis, reincarnation, romantic love and crude sexual fantasy.

> Schiller began to feel a little security. Even if the Supreme Court took back their stay and Gary was executed in a week or so, these letters still offered the story. He not only had the man's reason for dying but Romeo and Juliet and life after death. It might even be enough for a screen writer.

When Schiller's financial backers, ABC, drop out, he takes on the financial risk himself, aiming to collect a mass of documentation about the Gary Gilmore case, which can be handed over to a professional writer who will make a book out of it. At some point it dawns on the reader of *The Executioner's Song* that this *is* the book. Whatever odium attaches to Schiller, therefore, as an exploiter of Gary Gilmore's death, must be shared at one remove by Mailer. Mailer deals with this problem, and with the problem of his own belatedness upon the scene, boldly and effectively, by putting Larry Schiller, warts and all, in the foreground of "Eastern Voices". Thus Schiller performs the role that Mailer himself, ironically distanced by third-person narration, performs in his earlier books of reportage: not merely a reflector of events, but a consciousness in which the ethics and pragmatics of the writing project itself are laid bare. Schiller is in fact one of Mailer's finest character-creations – egotistical, unscrupulous, but human, comic and alive. Here he is, having snatched a quick vacation in Hawaii to appease his girlfriend Stephanie, dealing with bad news on the telephone from Gilmore's lawyer; the insurers of one of Gilmore's victims have filed an order for him to make a deposition, which threatens Schiller's monopoly over his story:

"I want you to go right into Court. If you can't block the deposition, at least file a motion that it's got to be put in bond." He smacked his fist against the night table, feeling a whole kinship with the notion of bond. "The tapes from that meeting," he said, "have got to be sealed right in the jail, and the Court has to give an order that they're not to be transcribed for so many months, blah blah, you understand what I mean, et cetera." Stephie was ready to kill him. Here it was supposed to be a vacation, and he was living on the phone. "Is this what it's going to be like when we get married?" she cried out. Was she just another woman? Was she a business deal? Schiller waved her off. Over the wire, he was practically writing out the motion. What a relief when he learned a couple of days later that the judge agreed to seal the stuff in wax, literally, until March.

It is impossible not to admire in some degree Schiller's energy, determination and resourcefulness, or to remain completely aloof from the excitement of his wheeling and dealing. On the other hand the moral ambivalence of his position is clear, and clear to himself.

In order to get Gilmore to entrust him with the rights to his story, he must form a friendly relationship with him, but the story will have maximum value only if Gary dies at the end of it – and can one wish for a friend's, or a client's death? When Gary's brother puts the question bluntly to him, Schiller has an answer ready: "I'm here to record history, not to make it." But even as he first formulated that defence, he had the unspoken thought: "Actually, I have become part of it. All around me. I'm becoming part of the story." Like Boswell in the case of John Reid, Schiller found he had invested more of himself than he knew in the life and death of Gary Gilmore.

Whatever the impurity of Schiller's motives, his judgement of the literary potential of the Gary Gilmore story was not misplaced, and one can understand why Norman Mailer put aside his own novel-in-progress to take it on. For the abiding impression this book leaves, with me at least, is of the remarkably "literary" quality of so many of its source materials, both major and minor.

The sexual relationship between Gary and Nicole, which physical separation raised to the pitch of the romantic sublime, was of course the most important of these "gifts" to the writer, because it was structural: establishing a fundamental antithesis between inside and outside prison – then, when Nicole is confined to a psychiatric ward after her suicide attempt, between two kinds of prison, so that from being a Romeo and Juliet they become a kind of Eloise and Abelard.

On the night when he committed his first murder, Gary was driving Nicole's schizophrenic sister April around in his pick-up truck, and her distracted Gertrude Stein-like remarks provide a weirdly appropriate surrealistic chorus to his actions (e.g. "It's hard to get along if you have to wait too long. The rooms get narrow and very often there is a dog").

As the story draws towards its close, the gratuitous ironies and equivalences and symbols multiply amazingly. During the night before Gary's execution, while an extraordinary vigil-cum-party is in progress in his cell, the ACLU persuade an eccentric judge to make a last-minute stay of execution. The Attorney General's staff retaliate with a writ of Mandamus, which will have to be heard by three judges at a higher court in Denver.

In the early hours of the morning, representatives of both sides, and one of the judges, fly over the Rockies through a storm in a small uninsured prop plane. There seems a high probability that they will all get killed in this frantic legal battle over Gary Gilmore's life, and though they make it safely to Denver, the judge has shortened his life expectancy by taking up smoking again under the strain of the flight. The stay is quashed, a last desperate appeal to the Supreme Court fails, and Gary Gilmore goes before the firing squad (his choice of death) only a little behind schedule. Larry Schiller, one of five people Gilmore was allowed to invite to witness his execution, discovers when he gets inside the prison that he has forgotten his notebook, and has to use his cheque-book as a substitute. The prince of cheque-book journalism, compelled to write his notes on the backs of cheques! In a work of fiction the irony would seem too heavy, but if you believe it actually happened it takes your breath away.

Mailer describes *The Executioner's Song* as a "dare I say it, true life story", and "as accurate as one could make it". We know, of course, and Mailer acknowledges, that absolute truth is never attainable in human affairs; but the basic contract the non-fiction novelist makes with his readers, the guarantee that his story is based entirely on verifiable sources, does enable him to exert over them the spell of the classic realistic novel, which has been so assiduously deconstructed and to an extent discredited by contemporary criticism. *The Executioner's Song* demonstrates the undiminished power of empirical narrative to move, instruct, and delight, to provoke pity and fear, and to extend our human understanding. It is remarkable, not for the originality of its conception – *In Cold Blood* retains that prize – but for the professional skill and self-discipline with which it is composed. This is easy to underestimate. There is a nice moment in *The Armies of the Night* when Robert Lowell says, a shade patronizingly, to Mailer, "I really think you are the best journalist in America," and Mailer replies, "Well, Cal . . . there are days when I think of myself as the best writer in America." *The Executioner's Song* certainly does not weaken that claim.

Getting at the Truth (1981)

The longest item in *Music for Chameleons*, a collection of "New Writing" by Truman Capote,* is entitled "Handcarved Coffins: A Nonfiction Account of an American Crime". It is described on the dust jacket as "the true story" of "the brutal crimes of a real-life murderer", and has just been serialized in the *Sunday Times* as a "true account of murder in a small American town".

The chief business of this review will be to argue that "Handcarved Coffins" is not a true story of actual crime, but a work of literary fiction. There are two grounds for the judgment – neither sufficient in itself, but in combination irresistible. First, there is the inherent implausibility of the events narrated, and the absence of any circumstantial data about them that might be verified. Secondly, there is the very literary "feel" of the whole text: that is, the experienced reader recognizes, as he works his way through it, structural features that are characteristic of literary fictions in general, and of the classic detective story in particular. "Handcarved Coffins" therefore raises some very interesting questions of literary theory, such as: what is "literariness" and what is "fictionality" and what is the relationship between these two categories, and what difference does it make to our reading of a narrative if it claims to be "true", and what difference if we reject that claim?

Such questions are bound to be raised by the kind of writing variously called the "non-fiction novel", "faction" and the "New Journalism". If Truman Capote did not exactly invent it (it goes back at least as far as Defoe) he may claim to have initiated a contemporary vogue for the genre with his masterly *In Cold Blood: A True Account of a Multiple*

*T. Capote, *Music for Chameleons* (Hamish Hamilton, 1981).

Murder and its Consequences (1966), inspiring a number of similar exercises by other American writers that are conscientiously surveyed by Ronald Weber in *The Literature of Fact*,* a book which is itself factually rather than theoretically illuminating. One of the most recent, and perhaps most distinguished examples of the genre was Norman Mailer's *The Executioner's Song*. Capote has some sly digs at Mailer in the preface to *Music for Chameleons*, observing that Mailer, after originally describing the experiment of *In Cold Blood* as "a failure of imagination", himself went on to write some very successful and highly profitable non-fiction novels, "though he has always been very careful not to describe them as non-fiction novels."

Technically, the two rivals have developed in opposite directions, *In Cold Blood* was written in a style of austere, Flaubertian impersonality, the author revealing nothing of his own feelings about the actions and persons represented, and this was a source of scandal to some readers. (Was it Kenneth Tynan who observed sourly that the only cold blood in the book was the author's? In this connection it is interesting that in one of the short pieces in *Music for Chameleons* Capote reveals that he vomited after witnessing the hangings of Hickcock and Smith so clinically described in *In Cold Blood*.) Mailer, of course, put his own flamboyant ego and highly rhetorical voice in the foreground of *The Armies of the Night, Miami and the Siege of Chicago* and of *Fire on the Moon*; and it was only in *The Executioner's Song* that he imitated Capote's impersonal, character-focalized style of reporting. (It is, incidentally, perverse of Professor Weber to regret the absence of Mailer's own persona from this book, since it was forced upon him by the circumstance that he did not himself witness the main events of the drama.)

Capote, meanwhile, has moved towards a more confessional, I-centred form of writing. His next major project after *In Cold Blood*, as he tells us in the preface to *Music for Chameleons*, was "a variation on the non-fiction novel", a candid, uncensored chronicle about himself and his friends in high and literary society entitled *Answered Prayers* ("More tears are shed over answered prayers than unanswered ones" – St Thérèse). Some parts of this work were published in *Esquire* in 1975–6 and were received with disappointment by the critics, and with anger by those whose private lives were exposed to public gaze. Violation of privacy and risk of libel are ethical and legal issues that inevitably arise from writing of this kind. Professor Weber explains that the New Journalists usually obtain "releases" from everyone concerned before

* R. Weber, *The Literature of Fact: Literary Non-fiction in American Writing* (Ohio University Press, 1980).

publishing – a process that can be very expensive, time-consuming and frustrating; Capote seems not to have bothered. In 1977, he confides, he stopped writing *Answered Prayers* because he was suffering "a creative and a personal crisis at the same time". He totally lost faith in his own writing:

> I read every word I'd ever published and decided that never, not once in my writing life, had I completely exploded all the energy and aesthetic excitements that material contained . . . The problem was: how can a writer successfully combine within a single form – say the short story – all he knows about writing? For that was why my work was often insufficiently illuminated: the voltage was there, but by restricting myself to the techniques of whatever form I was working in, I was not using everything I knew about writing – all I'd learned from film scripts, plays, reportage, poetry, the short story, novellas, the novel.

Capote then proceeded to experiment with a new synthesis of these different kinds of writing, of which *Music for Chameleons* contains the first fruits. (A revised version of *Answered Prayers* according to the same principles is, we are assured, in progress.)

The main formal features of this new style are two: the placing of the authorial persona in the foreground of the narrative; and the frequent use of a format that combines direct speech (presented as in a dramatic script, with occasional "stage directions") with interpolated passages of description or summary that are sometimes written in the present tense appropriate to a screenplay, and sometimes in the past tense of conventional narrative. Of the thirteen pieces in this collection, only "Mojave", a coolly ironic tale of sexual hang-ups among the Manhattan rich, could be described as a conventional short story. It begins:

> At 5 p.m. that winter afternoon she had an appointment with Dr Bentsen, formerly her psychoanalyst and currently her lover. When their relationship had changed from the analytical to the emotional, he insisted, on ethical grounds, that she cease to be his patient. Not that it mattered. He had not been of much help as an analyst, and as a lover – well, once she had watched him running to catch a bus, two hundred and twenty pounds of shortish, fiftyish, frizzly-haired, hip-heavy, myopic Manhattan Intellectual, and she had laughed: how was it possible that she could love a man so ill-humoured, so ill-favoured, as Ezra Bentsen? The answer was she didn't; in fact, she disliked him. But at least she didn't associate him with resignation and despair. She feared her husband; she was not afraid of Dr Bensten. Still, it was her husband she loved.

Why do we instantly classify this as fictional discourse? Mainly, of course, because the narrative is focalized through a character who is not the unspoken "I" from which the discourse originates, though that invisible narrator subtly intensifies the ironies of the character's situation by the condensations, antitheses and surprising swerves of his exposition, producing that harmonious balance of identification and detachment – engrossing without being disturbing – characteristic of a certain kind of sophisticated modern short-story writing (one especially associated with the *New Yorker*, where the young Capote learnt his craft). In principle there is no reason why this should not be an example of the New Journalism, applying rhetorical techniques perfected in the short story to the depiction of a real person; but the absence of explicit clues to the historicity of the woman (a well-known name, for example), and the intensely confidential, compromising nature of the subject matter, makes this inherently unlikely. Only fictional discourse usually claims this familiarity with the shameful and absurd secrets of another's erotic life; and we read this text unhesitatingly, therefore, as fiction.

The other short pieces in *Music for Chameleons* are all, in one way or another, autobiographical in mode: the source of the narrative is an "I" specifically identified as Truman Capote himself, and he functions as an "actant" as well as a narrator. Some of the pieces are anecdotes from his past: for instance, "Dazzle", a memoir of his Deep South childhood, of his desperate and reckless attempt to bribe a local "witch" to make him into a girl; or "Lamp in a Window", in which the fairy-tale benevolence of an old lady who generously gives him shelter for the night in a remote country place is given a grotesque twist by the discovery that her deep-freeze is packed with dead cats, her former pets. The latter part of the collection consists of "conversational portraits" in dialogue form; an interview with Robert Beausoleil, the associate of Charles Manson; an afternoon spent with an off-duty Marilyn Monroe (whose language, if Capote is to be believed, was far from ladylike); a day spent accompanying a black (or, as she prefers to be called, coloured) cleaning woman as she visits her clients' empty New York apartments, fortified by frequent inhalations of marijuana.

This last-mentioned piece is representative of Capote's "new writing" in the way it hesitates on the boundary between fact and fiction. One may believe that it is substantially true while suspecting that it has been improved by art. There is something suspiciously literary about the gradation in dramatic interest of the three visits Mary Sanchez and Capote make to the three apartments (three is itself, of course, an archetypal narrative frequency). The first is the squalid pad of a man estranged from his wife, littered with countless empty vodka miniatures (it turns out that he is an airline pilot – "O my God," says Capote, a frequent air-traveller). The second belongs to a neurotic lady journalist who has ostentatiously left a specimen of her Erica-Jongish poetry rolled into her typewriter, and a pink plastic vibrator in her bathroom cabinet. In the third episode, Capote and his companion, now high as kites on Mary's powerful grass, raid the refrigerator of the stuffy Mr and Mrs Berkowitz, and are interrupted in the middle of a bacchanalian dance by the outraged owners, who turn up just a little too neatly on cue. Still, it's an entertaining and touching story, which communicates vividly the charwoman's view of the underside of her clients' lives and at the same time draws a warm and convincing portrait of the woman herself.

It would still stand up as a text if it were demonstrated that it was entirely fictitious – and that seems to be the vital criterion of value in writing of this kind. However much of an emotional charge it may derive from the reader's belief that he is reading a true story – and in cases like *In Cold Blood* and *The Executioner's Song* that is considerable – the text should not, ultimately, depend on such extratextual support to obtain our "willing suspension of disbelief". George Orwell's "essays" "A Hanging" and "Shooting an Elephant" are classic examples. As Orwell's recent biographer, Bernard Crick, and Stansky and Abrahams before him, have shown, it is far from certain that Orwell ever witnessed a hanging or shot an elephant; but that question, however interesting to biographers, does not seem relevant to those texts' status as literature. It seems very important, however, to decide whether "Handcarved Coffins" is, as it claims to be, a work of non-fiction, because as a work of fiction it would not rate very high.

"Handcarved Coffins" begins in a motel room in an unidentified small town in a "Western State", in March 1975. The narrator, Truman Capote, is talking to a detective, Jake Pepper, from the State Bureau of Investigation, who has been investigating, for the past five years, a series of bizarre and baffling murders in the community. Capote explains that he has been in contact with Pepper by telephone for most of this time, but has come now to the scene of the crime to get the whole story.

> And so it was that I found myself one cold March night sitting with Jake Pepper in his motel room on the wintry, windswept outskirts of this forlorn little Western town. Actually, the room was pleasant, cosy; after all, it had been Jake's home for about five years . . .

Devotees of Conan Doyle will recognize here a condensation of some characteristic features of the Sherlock Holmes stories. These stories have been subjected to illuminating structural analysis by, among others, the Soviet semiotician, Yuri Scheglov, and L. M. O'Toole, Reader at the University of Essex; and in what follows I am indebted to the latter's article, "Analytic and Synthetic Approaches to Narrative Structure: Sherlock Holmes and 'The Sussex Vampire'" (in *Style and Structure in Literature*, ed. Roger Fowler, Blackwell, Oxford, 1977). As Scheglov points out, the Sherlock Holmes stories have a very predictable structure of narrative sequences, invariably beginning with a first report of the mystery to be solved in the cosy intimacy of the fog-shrouded Baker Street flat, followed by a visit to the scene of the crime, usually the well-appointed country house of some member of the upper classes, for further investigation of, and perhaps a new development in, the enigma. The atmospheric contrast between cosy interiors and threatening or inclement exteriors as a context for the investigation is important, because the genre, according to Scheglov, depends on a binary opposition between Security and Adventure for its appeal:

> It is the writer's task to look for conditions which will permit the foreground heroes (i.e. Holmes and Watson) simultaneously to receive a physical and spiritual "shock" by getting involved in all kinds of dramas and adventures, and yet not to quit their normal element, not to yield in any way their accustomed comforts, to enjoy full immunity . . . This world, uniting the terrifying and the safe, movement with tranquillity, discomfort with comfort, offers a combination of conditions in which the most sober of citizens would agree, would even volunteer, to have adventures and to come face to face with danger and horrors and so on.

Capote has of course, whether consciously or intuitively, subtly modified and combined the components of the model: thus Capote himself in one way performs the function of Holmes – the outsider who is brought to the scene of the crime by a baffled client; but the client in this case is the detective, who thinks he has solved the crime but cannot bring the culprit to book. In relation to Pepper, therefore, Capote also plays the part of Watson, Holmes's naive "feed", and the chronicler of the adventure.

O'Toole, while readily accepting the aptness of the Security/Adventure antithesis to the Holmes stories, regards it as one realization of a deeper structural opposition between Reason and the Irrational – Holmes's feats of detection representing the "triumph" of the former over the latter. In either formulation, the opposition is neatly encapsulated in the oxymoronic title of the story O'Toole analyses, "The Sussex Vampire", in which the associations of the Home Counties (Security, Reason) collide shockingly with those of Transylvania (Adventure, the Irrational) in a single phrase. Capote's title is a similar oxymoron, the homely, pleasant art-and-craft connotations of "handcarved" unexpectedly modifying the menacing and ominous "coffins". And the sequence of violent deaths that Jake Pepper relates to Truman Capote, as "a hard wind whipping the window announced that winter was still with us", is certainly a challenge to reason:

> JAKE: Eight murders, and not a single clue that would link the victims together to produce some semblance of a motive. Nothing. Except those three little handcarved coffins. I said to myself: No! No, it can't be! There's a *mind* behind all this, a reason.

The first to die were a married couple called Roberts, a lawyer and his wife who worked for him. One day they received through the mail a miniature coffin carved from balsam wood, containing a snapshot of themselves. A month later, getting into their car one sunny morning to drive to their office, they were attacked by amphetamine-injected rattlesnakes. They were found shut inside the car, hideously swollen and disfigured. Here the first spasm of empirical doubt makes itself felt. The account implies that both people, entering the car simultaneously from opposite sides, got inside and shut both doors before either of them noticed the amphetamine-crazed snakes. That seems improbable, to say the least. Later in the text we are told that the Robertses died on 5 September 1970. Doing a little detective work of my own, I discovered that that date fell on a Saturday. I suppose it is possible that a country town lawyer and his wife-assistant might go to their office on a Saturday morning, though it seems unlikely; less likely still that a murderer, setting a trap for them as they leave for work, should choose a Saturday, rather than an ordinary weekday, for the attempt.

Three months later, a couple called Baxter were burned to death in their cellar, with two chance guests, by an act of arson. It was not known whether they had received a coffin. But Clem Anderson, an old college friend of Jake's, did receive one, with a picture of himself driving his homemade jeep, and was frightened by it. He was unable to think what connection he might have with the other victims until one evening he tells Jake that it might have something to do with the local river. But the next day, before he has time to amplify this hint, he is dead, decapitated by a sharpened wire strung across the road along which he drives home in his jeep, a vehicle without superstructure or windshield.

Apart from the implausibility of this method of killing working with such perfect precision, and the pat irony of its timing, the personal bond between Jake and Anderson provides a suspiciously literary motivation for Jake's increasingly emotional commitment to solving the mystery. The next victim, however, is a rather unsavoury character, a doctor poisoned by nicotine via his own favourite indigestion mixture. At this point in his narrative, Pepper mentions to Capote the name of the man he suspects: Quinn. After reading aloud a misanthropic passage by Mark Twain, Jake Pepper exclaims: "Detestable. Malicious. A nasty mind. Yessir, that describes Quinn perfectly." There must be some superstition about the letter "Q", so many nasty, malicious, detestable characters in literature have names that begin with it: Quilp, Quint, Quilty . . . Jake Pepper's name has appropriately contrasting connotations – country-and-western homeliness, a warm but volatile temperament.

Having mentioned the suspect's name, Jake Pepper refuses to proceed any further with his narrative until the next day, when he has arranged to take Truman Capote to meet a woman called Addie Mason in the town. Thus Capote's, and vicariously the reader's, curiosity and suspense are prolonged. The scene shifts to the comfortable house of Addie, a spinster schoolmistress, and her widowed sister (this shift corresponds to the movement from Baker Street to the country in the Sherlock Holmes stories). A sumptuous meal is served, and again an atmospheric contrast is evoked between the cosy interior and the inhospitable exterior where (somewhere) the murderer lurks: "Snow, fluttering at the windows like torn lace curtains, emphasized the comforts of the room, the warmth of the fire, the redness of the wine." Addie describes to Capote how she received a coffin, sought the help of Jake Pepper, and worked out the connection between herself and the other victims: all had been members of a local committee formed to adjudicate on a proposal to divert the local river for irrigation purposes The propery owner who lost most by their approval of the scheme was Robert Quinn.

As this narrative proceeds, Truman Capote infers that Jake and Addie are in love, and he learns shortly after that they plan to marry. Thus the threatened next victim of the murderer whom Jake is pursuing is the very person dearest to him in the world. This doubling of the motivation, superimposing a romantic theme on top of the law-and-order theme, is typical of traditional prose fiction, of what is sometimes called the classic realist text. It is the literary equivalent of Freudian "over-determination", and betrays an anxiety on the author's part to hold the reader's interest at all costs, by providing an excess of reasons for our sympathetic identification with the "good" characters. It comes as no surprise to discover that, in contrast to Addie's homely looks and wholesome sexuality, Quinn's wife is embittered, alcoholic, and half-Spanish; or, later, that he has a mistress and four illegitimate children.

Pepper soon drives Capote out to Quinn's ranch. It seems that in spite of all the grounds for suspicion, Pepper has not succeeded in convincing his superiors that Quinn is the killer – or else Quinn is being protected by powerful friends in the State government. Accordingly, Pepper is reduced to making social visits to Quinn, hoping to trick him into making a damaging admission, and he takes Capote out to the ranch for this purpose. This corresponds to the sequence "Holmes confronts and unmasks the villain" in the classic archetype. As Capote is introduced to Quinn,

> the sight of him startled me. *I knew Mr Quinn.* I was positive, I would have sworn on my own heartbeat that somehow, and undoubtedly long ago, I had encountered Robert Harley Quinn, and that together we had, in fact, shared an alarming experience, an adventure so disturbing, memory had kindly submerged it.

This is a coincidence so outrageously improbable that no reader's credulity could survive it. However, as we read on, we discover that Quinn merely *reminds* Capote of a very similar man, a fanatical religious preacher in the Deep South, who terrified the five-year-old Capote by trying to baptize him by immersion. Having doubted, the reader may now be reassured to trust the tale, not only in this particular, but in all others – that, I take it, is the author's hope. The sequence also motivates Capote's intuitive agreement with Jake's identification of Quinn as the murderer.

Quinn, however, avoids giving away clinching proof, and Pepper, obsessed with the desire to catch him, is constrained to use his beloved fiancée as bait, instead of removing her from danger. Truman Capote goes to Europe for a vacation, and his return is delayed. When he finally gets back he learns that Addie was drowned two days before her wedding day – accidentally, according to the coroner's verdict. Jake is of course convinced that Quinn was responsible, though Truman Capote, for reasons that are not entirely clear, is not. This causes an estrangement between the two men, as Jake, increasingly isolated and on the edge of breakdown, bangs his head against the brick wall of public scepticism and indifference. The narrative frays out into a series of notes and jottings from Capote's diary covering a number of years, until eventually Jake is due for retirement, his quest unfulfilled. Truman Capote travels to the small Western town for a farewell reunion, and then makes a solitary visit to the Quinn ranch. There he finds Quinn fishing his river, thigh-deep in water, like the fanatical preacher, and like him also in being convinced of the consonance of his own will and God's:

> "The way I look at it is this: it was the hand of God." He raised his own hand, and the river, viewed between his spread fingers, seemed to weave between them like a dark ribbon. "God's work. His will."

This is how the story ends: the image of the river, delicately alluding to the classical mythology of the Styx and the Fates, offers an aesthetic conclusion in place of a narrative resolution of the plot. In this respect, of course, "Handcarved Coffins" deviates radically from the classic detective story, in which all mystery is dispersed, Reason triumphs over the Irrational and Right over Wrong. "Handcarved Coffins" ends with the culprit still at large, triumphant and invulnerable, while the just man, Jake Pepper, is left broken and disillusioned.

Perhaps it is the consonance of this ending with the cynicism and despair contemporary Americans feel about their public life that explains why American reviewers of "Handcarved Coffins" have, as far as I can ascertain, either accepted its claim to be a true story, or expressed only tentative doubts. James Wolcott, in the *New York Review of Books*, for instance, wrote "you begin to wonder whether fact and fiction aren't bubbling together in the same pot". Professor Weber quotes Philip Roth's remark that "the American writer in the middle of the twentieth century has his hands full in trying to understand, and then render, and then make *credible*, much of the American reality". Truth is so much stranger than fiction, these days, that the reading public will apparently give credence to the most hackneyed and sentimental stereotypes of fiction masquerading as fact.

It is certain that no intelligent reader would believe that "Handcarved Coffins" was a true story for a moment if it were not subtitled a "non-fiction account" (a phrase that borrows considerable authority from the precedent of the same author's *In Cold Blood*) and described as a "true story" by its publishers – for one does not expect dust-jacket blurbs to lie. I thought it prudent to inquire of the British and American publishers whether they had any evidence to support this assertion, and received courteous but guarded replies to the effect that they had relied exclusively on the assurances of the author. They have been very trusting. Of course, as a property, "Handcarved Coffins" is worth a lot more as a true story than as a work of fiction; which is to say that as a work of literature with serious pretensions it is worth very little. We may be interested by the spectacle of life imitating bad art, but not by bad art (i.e. over-familiar, exhausted conventions) proposing to imitate life.

Capote would, I suppose, justify his proceedings as a kind of hoax, or game with the reader; and there are certainly several clues in the text to this effect. The narrator-actant, Truman Capote, is, for instance, always ahead of the reader in voicing doubts about the plausiblity of the story. "The amazing thing is," he says to Jake at the outset, "nobody seems to know anything about this case. It's had almost no publicity." His comment on the murder of Clem Anderson is "preposterous". There are several literary allusions which should put the reader on his guard, especially in this passage:

TC: *A Coffin For Dimitrios.*
JAKE: What say?
TC: A book by Eric Ambler. A thriller.
JAKE: Fiction? (I nodded; he grimaced.) You really read that junk?
TC: Graham Greene was a first-class writer. Until the Vatican grabbed him. After that, he never wrote anything as good as *Brighton Rock*. I like Agatha Christie, love her. And Raymond Chandler is a great stylist, a poet. Even if his plots are a mess.
JAKE: Junk. Those guys are just daydreamers – squat at a type-writer and jerk themselves off, that's all they do.

A Coffin For Dimitrios is the American title of Eric Ambler's *The Mask of Dimitrios* (1939,) a novel about a thriller writer who becomes involved in a "real" murder mystery through his acquaintance with a police officer. This seems to be a heavy hint that "Handcarved Coffins" has its origins in fiction rather than fact, as does the allusion to Agatha Christie whose *Ten Little Indians* (originally *Ten Little Niggers*) has a similar so-many-down-so-many-to-go plot. The muddled reference to Graham Greene (he was converted to Roman Catholicism, if that is what is meant by "grabbed by the Vatican", in 1926; *Brighton Rock* (1938), was in fact the first of his novels to deal explicitly with Catholicism; his next novel, *The Power and the Glory*, was actually condemned by the Holy Office) is of less obvious relevance. But the final derisive comment on writers of fiction is plainly a nudge aimed at the credulous reader. Only the scenario format conceals the author's grin.

The title story of *Music for Chameleons* describes a conversation between Truman Capote and a patrician lady of Martinique. Chameleons scamper about the terrace where they sit sipping absinthe-flavoured tea. She comments: "Such exceptional creatures. The way they change colour . . . And did you know they are very fond of music . . . You don't believe me?" She goes to the piano in her "cool, Caribbean saloon" and begins to play. Sure enough, the chameleons accumulate at her feet, "a sensitive, absorbed audience for the music". But of course this "proof" is purely a literary illusion dependent on the credibility of Capote's own text. As if to reinforce the point, he himself claims a few lines later to have seen ghosts in Haiti in broad daylight, " 'picking bugs off coffee plants.' She accepts this as fact." *Music for Chameleons* is indeed full of tall stories asking to be accepted as fact, full of characters who enjoy testing each other's credulity, and their own narrative persuasiveness. Thus Marilyn Monroe tells Truman Capote a story about Errol Flynn taking his penis out of his fly at a party and thumping out the tune of

"The Star-Spangled Banner" with it on the piano, while he counters with a reminiscence of having once seduced Flynn. "That's not much of a story," says Marilyn. "Not worth mine – not by a long shot." By "her" story she means not the one about Flynn, but the one about herself and Arthur Miller, which Capote is trying to winkle out of her. But by "worth" does she mean equivalent in scandalous truth or equivalent in narrative interest, the "pleasure of the text"? That is the distinction Capote teases the reader with throughout *Music for Chameleons*, thus making, out of some fairly lightweight writing, a book that continuously beguiles, and that lingers in the mind.

American English (1981)

In principle it was a good idea to make the latest addition* to the distinguished Oxford family of dictionaries published in America last year, and designed for American users, available to the British reading public. Because America is culturally dominant among the English-speaking nations, we are constantly bombarded in literature, film, TV and radio with words and phrases which are either peculiarly American (e.g. *sneakers, boondocks, rain check*) or have different meanings in American English from the ones we are familiar with (e.g. *vest, trunk* and *stroller*). These are fairly venerable examples and probably most educated British adults know that they mean, respectively: plimsolls, wild or remote rural provinces, a ticket stub entitling the bearer to readmission to a postponed sports event, a waistcoat, a car boot, and a pushchair. But younger people are likely to find them puzzling on first acquaintance; and in any case one symptom of America's cultural dominance is its creativity in the production of new words, phrases and usages. So there is certainly a genuine need for a comprehensive and up-to-date dictionary of American English outside America itself.

The *Oxford American Dictionary* (henceforward *OAD*) does not, however, meet that need very satisfactorily; nor does it put its competitors in the shade. I have been comparing it with the new *Collins English Dictionary* (*CED*) which costs about the same, and ambitiously attempts to embrace all the major varieties of contemporary English, and a "new updated edition" of the Funk and Wagnalls *Standard Desk Dictionary* (*FW*), an American dictionary available in this country at the bargain price of £4.95.

* *Oxford American Dictionary*, compiled by Eugene Ehrlich, Stuart Berg Flexner, Gorten Carruth, Joyce M. Hawkins (Oxford University Press, 1980).

The *OAD* is a medium-sized dictionary with only 70,000 entries, approximately, compared to *FW*'s 100,000 and *CED*'s 162,000. It is also conservatively edited, by which I mean two things: it includes some six hundred mildly but firmly prescriptive notes on correct usage (e.g. "Careful writers do not use *contact* as a verb. Instead of *contacting someone* they *call* or *write* or *visit* him") and it excludes all taboo words and a great deal of "vulgar" slang. I have no objection in principle to the notes on correct usage, which are generally sound and sensible, but they are not always applicable to the British user (it is, for example, much less acceptable to *write someone* than to *contact someone* in our language community). More seriously, it is precisely in the area of colloquial, informal and vulgar usage, where the *OAD* is weakest, that British users will be most likely to consult it.

The reader of a sentence like "We're gonna stick it to them mothers", which I take from Donald Barthelme's much admired novel, *The Dead Father* (1975), will look in vain in the *OAD* for the meanings of *stick it* and *mothers* (*CED* has the latter). The Englishman who offers to *knock up* his American female house guest early in the morning will discover in the *CED* but not in the *OAD* why she bursts into hysterical laughter. The *OAD* does not acknowledge the existence of *rubber* in the sense of condom, or for that matter of *condom*. It includes *ass* as in the sense of bottom, but not *piece of ass*. All these missing words are to be found in *CED*, and some in *FW*. It is difficult to understand why the *New York Times* described the *OAD* as "sassy". It is just about the least saucy dictionary I have ever come across.

The explanation, I suspect, is that the *OAD* is aimed in part at the junior end of the educational market, and American schools, or their PTAs, are notoriously puritanical about the reading matter they will approve. Reticence, however, will not account for all the omissions. The *OAD* omits not only *rubber* in the contraceptive sense, but *rubbers* in the sense of waterproof clothing and footwear. It omits the verb *pin* as used in that quintessentially American campus betrothal rite, by which a boy signals his steady attachment to a girl by giving her his fraternity pin. It omits *to go*, meaning wrapped ready to be taken away, as applied to food (e.g. "One cheeseburger to go, please"). It omits *bum's rush* which is not as vulgar as it may sound to British ears. All these words and phrases may be found in *CED* and *FW*.

Let us look at the credit side of the balance sheet. The *OAD* scored maximum points with four idioms noted in a recent episode of "Kojak": *stake-out* (police surveillance of a building), *bottom line* (the final consequence), *down the tube* (wasted, ruined) and the verb *poormouth* (meaning to claim poverty as an excuse). *CED* has *stake-out*; otherwise it and *FW* were of no assistance with these idioms. *OAD* includes *beautiful people* (well defined as "wealthy trendsetters, fashionable people") and *grunts*, meaning infantrymen, both omitted by *CED* and *FW*. But these successes do not alter the fact that the *OAD* makes a disappointing general impression.

My copy came with a publicity handout, evidently designed to do the lazy reviewer's work for him, which lists some forty words or phrases that might cause difficulty for the native Briton. Only seven of these are not to be found in the *CED* and *FW*, which is a pretty good score for the former, though not for the latter, which is supposed to be an American dictionary. They are: *granola* (a kind of muesli), *pantyhose* (tights), *brown-bagging* (taking lunch to work), *empty nesters* (a couple whose children have left home), *humongous* (a whimsical slang word for huge, tremendous, which I have never met before, and hope never to meet again), *on the fritz* (out of order) and *off the wall* (crazy, bizarre). The *OAD* does not, however, include the more recent use of *off the wall* in "psychobabble" to mean spontaneously (cf. Cyra McFadden's *The Serial*).

Words and phrases that are common to the *OAD* and the *CED* are often better defined in the latter. For example, the *CED*'s gloss on *funky* as a musical term ("passionate and soulful, reminiscent of early blues") is more precise than the *OAD*'s "uncomplicated, emotional"; while the *OAD* does not have the second, derived meaning noted by the *CED*: "pleasing or attractive especially in an exaggerated or camp manner". Nor does it have the *CED*'s etymology: "from FUNK², perhaps alluding to music that was smelly, that is, earthy, like early blues". Nor does the *OAD* have an equivalent entry for *CED*'s FUNK²: "In US slang, a strong foul odour [C17 in the sense: tobacco smoke: from *funk* (vb.) to smoke (tobacco) probably of French dialect origin; compare Old French *funkier* to smoke, from Latin *fumigare*]." The *OAD*'s lack of etymologies (which are provided, more briefly than in *CED*, in *FW*) is a very serious drawback for the British user, since half the fun of looking up a picturesque Americanism like *boondocks* is finding out its derivation. (*CED* and *FW* will tell you that it comes from the Tagalog word for mountain, *bundok*.)

The *OAD* is pleasantly, clearly printed, easy to handle and consult, and no doubt serves the purpose for which it was originally designed quite satisfactorily. School librarians in this country who feel the need for a dictionary of contemporary American English, but do not want their pupils to be able to look up rude words in it, could certainly do worse than add the *OAD* to their collection. But, lacking etymologies, pronunciation keys in the International Phonetic Alphabet, and entries for even mildly improper slang, the *OAD* is of very limited usefulness to the grown-up British user. For half the price you could buy the Funk and Wagnalls, which is about as comprehensive, though not so good on recent idioms, and has etymologies. For the same price you could buy the Collins, which compares very favourably in its coverage of American English and offers a great deal besides.

[*Postscript*: Honesty compels me to say that, in the years since this review was published, I have found the *Oxford American Dictionary*, for all its shortcomings, an invaluable reference book, especially when writing dialogue for American characters.]

Dam and Blast (1982)

The Dam Busters, shown on BBC Television one Sunday afternoon recently, must be the perfect war film for people like myself who don't really approve of war, or of the military mystique of competitive valour and unquestioning obedience to authority, or of the exploitation of these things for purposes of entertainment, but nevertheless go weak at the knees at the image of a flak-scarred Lancaster bomber coming in to land on a dandelion-strewn airfield at dawn somewhere in East Anglia in 1943.

I was four when World War II began, so I followed its fortunes with the simple patriotic pride and black-and-white morality which belongs to childhood. Since my father was in the Air Force (as a musician who prudently avoided going up in an aeroplane even once), I took a special interest in that arm of the Services, became a fairly adept plane-spotter, and operated an extensive military airfield on the top of the Morrison shelter which filled most of the front room of our London semi. I covered many sheets of paper depicting aerial battles in which Spitfires and Hurricanes unfailingly shot Messerschmitts and Heinkels out of the sky while Lancasters and Wellingtons dropped their bombs with unerring accuracy on German tanks and ships.

Later, of course, came the loss of innocence and the acquisition of knowledge: about the horrific firestorms of Dresden and other German cities, about the deliberate attacks on civilian populations, about the failure of mass bombing seriously to affect German morale and war production, and about the frightful toll in terms of Allied aircrew casualties. Patriotic pride was replaced by retrospective anger at those senior strategists, like Air Marshal Sir Arthur "Bomber" Harris, who from safe offices and Ops Rooms sent so many young men to futile and agonizing deaths.

The Dam Busters was made in 1954, when the myth of Bomber Command's strategic success was still relatively unscathed by revisionist historians. Harris is portrayed in it without criticism – indeed, as a kind of wise and benign Providence who gives the brilliant boffin, Barnes Wallis, the chance to realize his revolutionary idea for a bouncing bomb with which to shatter the Ruhr dams. The entire film is saturated in an archaic and class-ridden ideology of leadership, loyalty and courage derived from the public-school ethos, imperialistic adventure stories and memories of the First World War. Yet, for all that, it remains a decent film which it is possible to view today without too much irony. It is naive, but it is not hypocritical and it is not insensitive. Its effectiveness owes much, no doubt, to R. C. Sherriff's screenplay, for his classic drama of trench warfare in the First World War, *Journey's End*, had much the same strengths and limitations. The feature of *The Dam Busters* that grates most on the viewer in 1982 is that the hero's pet dog is called "Nigger" and that the name is adopted as the code word for a successful hit on the dams; and this is historical, not an invention of Sherriff's.

Why has *The Dam Busters* worn better than most examples of its genre and period? One reason is that it is singularly lacking in hatred, and that vicarious pleasure in violence which most war films, even those ostensibly "anti-war" in intention, tend to arouse in their audiences. There are no German corpses to gloat over here – indeed, there are scarcely any Germans. The target is a clean one – a huge, inanimate, uninhabited monolith; and the consequences of its destruction – the flooding of the Ruhr valleys – are depicted in a montage sequence almost entirely devoid of human figures. Only once do we glimpse four civilians fleeing from a flooded factory. (There is, of course, some cosmeticization of history involved here: according to Paul Brickhill, whose book *The Dam Busters* was a major source for the film, the raid caused the deaths of 1,294 people by drowning, the majority of them slave labourers and Russian prisoners of war.) Correspondingly, there is no attempt to harrow the audience with direct depictions of the last moments of those airmen whose planes are shot down.

All films about aerial warfare, and especially those concerned with bombing raids, tend towards the condition of chivalric romance. The basic structure of their narratives is what A. J. Greimas has called "disjunctive" – a story of departure and return, of which the Quest is the archetype. The Falklands War, incidentally, had the same narrative structure, from the British point of view, which partly explains why it gripped the imaginations of many people who did not approve of it. In this kind of story the hero and his companions venture out, away from secure home ground, into foreign and hostile territory, endure great sufferings and perform great acts of valour, then return home, exalted or chastened by the experience. In films about bombing raids this narrative structure is subjected to extreme temporal condensation: a bombing mission over Germany is an eight-hour-crusade. The emotional power of the story derives from the tension between the felt obligation to risk one's life and the desire to return home safely. In the bomber films this tension is dramatized in the characteristic sequence that cross-cuts between the heroes in the throes of the flak and the action over Germany, and the boffins, superior officers, ground staff, wives and girlfriends in England, who can do nothing but wait and bite their nails in rooms where the loudest noise is the ringing of a telephone or the chatter of Morse.*

Interestingly, there are no wives or girlfriends in *The Dam Busters*, just as there is never the slightest suspicion of obscenity or profanity in the dialogue. Here again, no doubt, we may detect the hand of R. C. Sheriff, for Brickhill makes clear that Squadron Leader Guy Gibson was married, and that the men under his command had normal heterosexual interests. One of the neatest touches in the screenplay comes when Gibson and his chief bombing officer are shown seeking some light relief from their training at a music hall. As the star of the show goes into her song-and-dance routine, Gibson (played by Richard Todd) sits up in his seat as though electrified: a piece of body language the seasoned cinema-goer is likely to interpret as a sign that "love interest" is about to be introduced. In fact, it soon becomes evident that Gibson's interest has been excited not by the girl but by the two spotlights trained on her, suggesting to him a solution to the problem of measuring altitude when flying too low for conventional instruments to function.

The thoroughgoing desexualization of the airmen reinforces the romantic and chivalric overtones of the story. In the Grail legend there is a stressed connection between male chastity and the successful completion of the Quest. Gibson's squadron is an élite group, a Round Table of airborne knights, whose Grail is the destruction of the great dams. The figure of Barnes Wallis fits into this archetypal scheme as a kind of benevolent Merlin, wielding the magical power of "science". "Wizard"

---

* According to the French narratologist invoked above, there are three basic types of narrative structure: (1) the disjunctive (2) the performative (*e.g.* the story of the tasks of Hercules), and (3) the contractual (*e.g.* the story of the Fall). It occurred to me after this piece was first published that *The Dam Busters* is quite as much a "performative" as a "disjunctive" story, since the task of destroying the dam is central to it, whereas in most Bomber Command films the effectiveness of the raid is less important than the survival of the airmen. This reflection does not, I think, invalidate Greimas's typology, but rather suggests that the more narrative types you can combine in a single story, the more powerful its effect on the audience is likely to be. The Falklands War, like the Trojan War, combined all three motives.

was, of course, the ultimate epithet of praise in RAF slang. According to Brickhill, Gibson actually reported to his superiors, "It was a wizard party," on his return from the raid. He doesn't say this in the film, in which, interestingly enough, the behaviour of all the returning airmen is considerably less exuberant than it was in reality.

I have suggested that *The Dam Busters* works partly by transposing a story of modern technological warfare into the key of chivalric romance, filtering out in the process most of the ugly and disturbing features of the real history it deals with. The surface of the film is, however, scrupulously realistic, even documentary, in style; and this allows it eventually to depart from the historical "fact" in the opposite direction, to state an unpalatable truth about war. The ending of the film is distinctly downbeat, and never fails to impress. The exhausted and emotionally-drained air-crew stagger from their planes. There is no cheering or backslapping, just the exchange of cigarettes and tight-lipped smiles between the survivors. Two men drag themselves back to their quarters, and collapse speechlessly onto their beds, fully dressed. The camera lingers on empty rooms whose occupants will not return. On the soundtrack a BBC announcer reports the success of the mission and concludes: "Eight of the Lancasters are missing." Barnes Wallis is shown shattered by this news: "Fifty-six men. If I had known it was going to be like this I'd never have started it." Gibson tries to comfort him: "Even if all those fellows had known from the beginning that they wouldn't be coming back, they would still have gone for it." But even if he really believed that, we certainly don't. The final note is one of loss, waste and regret. The last shot is of Gibson, still wearing his flying jacket, walking away from the camera, along a bleak path between barrack blocks, on his way to write letters of condolence.

Arguably, the real stars of the film are the Lancasters, which the director Michael Anderson and his cameraman photographed in black and white with great skill and artistry, posing their unmistakable profiles against the flat landscapes and huge skies of East Anglia to poignant effect, or showing their great wings thrillingly skimming the moonlit waters of river, lake and sea. To call the Lancaster a "photogenic" aircraft would be misleading – the epithet is more appropriate to the Spitfire. But the Lancaster had the beauty of functional engineering, and it was perfectly balanced in its proportions, with just the necessary touch of individuality in its protruding observation dome, jutting forward pugnaciously like the underhung jaw of a bulldog, that inspires affection as well as instant recognition.

That's how I feel about the Lancaster, anyway. To the men who flew them I have no doubt they were noisy, uncomfortable deathtraps. Put my sentiments down to nostalgia for childhood.

Readings and Lessons (1982)

Here are two books* about the Bible by two writers whose disciplinary base is secular literature rather than theology or scriptural exegesis. Dan Jacobson is Reader in English at University College London, as well as being a distinguished novelist. Robert Alter is Professor of Hebrew and Comparative Literature at the University of California, Berkeley. Both authors are Jewish. One might expect their books to have a lot in common. In fact their approach to the subject is entirely different.

Jacobson's *The Story of the Stories* is an extended polemical essay on the historical and ideological myth that lies behind the books of the Old Testament, and on its ramifications in the New. He concentrates on the Prophetic books, such as Deuteronomy and Isaiah, and admits that he thus neglects the narrative books which are particularly prized by those who read the Bible "as literature". Robert Alter, on the other hand, has such readers very much in mind, and concentrates on precisely those books of the Old Testament which Jacobson passes over. For Alter, narrativity is the very essence of the Bible (by which he means the Old Testament exclusively) and inseparable from its moral and spiritual import. Not only, he argues, were the writers of the Old Testament precursors of modern novelists; to approach such stories as those of Joseph, or David, or Balaam with the tools of modern criticism of fiction is the best way to apprehend the real profundity, subtlety and complexity of their meanings, which are often overlooked or obfuscated by the positivist historical approach of modern biblical scholarship.

Again, Jacobson's book is iconoclastic, Alter's recuperative. Jacobson's is directed at the "general reader", Alter's at the student of

* D. Jacobson, *The Story of the Stories: the Chosen People and Its God*. (Secker & Warburg, 1982).

R. Alter, *The Art of Biblical Narrative* (Allen & Unwin, 1981).

literature and/or the Bible. Jacobson writes as an amateur making a bold foray into intellectual territory already staked out by a formidable body of professional experts; Alter makes a take-over bid for that territory in the name of his own professionalism. Jacobson writes simply, directly, sometimes colloquially, with an effect of sincerity and avoidance of cant that reminds one of George Orwell. Robert Alter writes in the best mode of academic discourse: learned, eloquent, urbane, using technical jargon only when it seems useful and always with careful explanation. Both books are excellent of their kind, and well worth reading. They are not really comparable. Yet they complement each other splendidly; and, quite fortuitously, Robert Alter's book provides a kind of response to the challenge posited by Dan Jacobson's.

The challenge is directed at anyone, whether Jew or Christian (but principally the former), who considers that the Bible is in some sense a revelation of religious truth, of the nature of God and man's relation to God. Dan Jacobson is ethnically Jewish, but a non-believer. He starts from the rationalist and materialist assumption that Yaweh, the God of the Old Testament, and the role assigned to him in the history of Israel, is a fiction, and his interest is in trying to understand the motivation behind that fiction: why did the Jews make up this story about themselves and Yaweh, and what does it mean? Not, what did they think it meant, which is very obvious; but what does it really mean? Dan Jacobson cleaves to the dictum "Never trust the teller, trust the tale," which is, indeed, a cardinal principle of modern hermeneutics, from Freud and Nietzsche to Lévi-Strauss.

Jacobson begins by citing the sombre account, in Kings 2, of the evil reign of King Zedekiah, his rebellion against Nebuchadnezzar, the king of Babylon, the capture and destruction of Jerusalem and the beginning of the Babylonian exile. Zedekiah's personal fate was particularly horrible. "They slew the sons of Zedekiah before his eyes, and put out the eyes of Zedekiah, and bound him in fetters, and took him to Babylon." Dan Jacobson's comment on this passage is very acute. He points out that Zedekiah's wickedness has been described, earlier in the same passage, as "he did what was evil in the sight of [literally, "in the eyes of"] the Lord". Thus,

The man who did evil in the eyes of the Lord suffers the punishment of having his own eyes put out; but only after they have witnessed the sight he would most have wished to be spared. Furthermore, through the murder of his own children, the fact that he is to be the very last, the end point, of a long line of such wrongdoing kings, is presented dramatically to him, so to speak, as well as to us, the readers of the tale.

Here, at the very outset of his book, Dan Jacobson comes as near as he ever does to the method of Robert Alter, who delights in drawing out of the biblical texts just such echoes and parallels, which are brought into play by stylistic devices of repetition that may look, to a critical sensibility schooled in classical rhetoric, like clumsy and primitive redundancy (elegant variation and syntactical subordination could easily rob the description of Zedekiah's punishment of half its force). But in this small example Jacobson sees a key to the ideological macrostructure of the Old Testament. It is

> an illustration of that sense of remorseless *reciprocity* governing the processes of history which seems central to the biblical writers' moral and imaginative life, and hence to the way in which they perceived the world . . . Every act or condition, in this view, contains within it, and will sooner or later generate, its opposite; every deed and every claim will produce another that will balance it, or invert it, or reverse it . . .

In the account of Zedekiah's unsuccessful rebellion against Babylon, Jacobson is struck by the way that defeat for Israel is presented as a victory for Yaweh, because Israel has shown itself unworthy of Yaweh's special protection. Thus the infidel Nebuchadnezzar becomes the instrument of God, and the Israelites are punished for their sins by a symmetrical inversion of their first entry into the Promised Land.

That entry was achieved, Dan Jacobson reminds us in his next chapter, at the expense of the Promised Land's original inhabitants, the Canaanites; and it is hardly an exaggeration to say that he sees the entire "story of the stories" as growing from that germ, as a collective attempt to rationalize the guilt accruing to that occupation. To justify the seizure of the land, the Jews are defined as a race divinely chosen, under the special protection of the one true God, who sanctions the deed by denouncing the Canaanites as evil idolaters: "You shall tear down their altars, and break their pillars, and cut down their Asherim . . ." (Exodus 34: 13–16). When the Israelites themselves suffer the same fate, at the hands of Nebuchadnezzar, this is ostensibly because they have failed to deserve Yaweh's special favour by obeying his law; but the reciprocity of the two events suggests a kind of inevitability, the working out of a primal curse, more akin to the Fate of pagan tragedy. "The explicit moral is that the people of Israel fall into God's disfavour only when they disobey him; the tacit moral is that the very notion of having been chosen by such a God will produce the retribution appropriate to it."

Having invented a God who will sanction their territorial designs on other people, the Israelites become fearful of the power they themselves have invested in him, and seek to control it by the fiction of a Covenant. But the power cannot be tamed so easily. History being what it is, the

Israelites will experience inevitable fluctuations of fortune in random and unpredictable ways, but have condemned themselves to read into these events a terrific weight of moral and metaphysical meaning, of pride and guilt. They become victims of their own historical myth – "that pitiless sequence or alternation whereby the gain of the people of Israel has to be the loss of another, and vice versa, through all eternity". To escape this double bind, Judaism turned to apocalyptic fantasies of a world of peace and justice ruled over by a benevolent Jewish despotism, but this utopian promise was taken over by Christianity and developed, especially by Paul, in a new "story of the stories" in which the Jews were portrayed as having irredeemably forfeited God's favour by killing his Son – with grim historical consequences that we know all too well.

In the introduction to his book, Dan Jacobson explains that his curiosity about its subject was partly inspired by a wish "to understand better some aspects of the great catastrophe that fell upon the Jews of Europe in the 1940s". Though he does not spell it out explicitly, the conclusion he reached seems to be not unlike that which George Steiner recently put into the mouth of the arraigned Adolf Hitler in his novella *The Portage to San Cristobal of A. H.*, namely, that the Jews in a sense provided the conceptual framework which made their persecution possible. Though neither Steiner nor Jacobson implies that this exonerates the rest of humanity from responsibility for the Holocaust, it is a view profoundly shocking and indeed outrageous to orthodox Jewry, and perhaps only a Jewish writer could put it forward without being accused of anti-semitism. (In fact, Steiner has been fiercely attacked by Jewish critics, and no doubt Jacobson will be too.) Dan Jacobson's pessimistic reading of the history of Israel as an endless alternation of injustice perpetrated and injustice suffered has been strikingly reinforced by recent events in the Near East. But it would be misleading to suggest that, because his book is chiefly concerned with Jewish Scripture, its thesis only concerns the Jews. Jacobson sees the same fatal flaw in all ideologies, including some versions of Christianity and Marxism, which incorporate the idea of those who are chosen for a particular destiny, implying the existence of those who are not chosen, who are dispensable. As a South African, Dan Jacobson has personal experience of a Christian sect on whom the Old Testament model of the Chosen People who have made a covenant with God has had a particularly powerful and deplorable effect. And let us not forget that the recent massacre in Beirut, so chillingly reminiscent of an SS *Aktion* in a Polish ghetto, was, with whatever connivance by the Israeli authorities, actually perpetrated by people identified as "Christian".

The Story of the Stories is a brave, forceful, thought-provoking book.

But is not its argument, in the last analysis, a little too simple and reductive? Even Dan Jacobson himself seems to think so, and rather disarmingly shares his doubts with the reader in his closing pages. Putting his own account of the Bible beside the history of Judaism and Christianity, he asks himself, "Is it possible that these are the stories behind all that movement and passion? How could the evident confusions and illogicalities of the overarching story of the Hebrew Scriptures have had so great an effect on so many people?" His explanation is that those who have been affected by the Scriptures read them with faith, whereas he has read them simply "as stories". This he admits is "inadequate", though it is hard to know exactly what this concession amounts to – not, presumably, a recantation of the entire argument he has put forward, but an acknowledgment that those who start from different premisses will never be persuaded by it. I don't think, however, that we need accept this stalemate.

At the beginning of his study, Dan Jacobson puts his cards on the table: "If Yaweh is a human creation, as I believe him to be, then his actions and the utterances ascribed to him in his dealings with his people must reveal needs and fears which his creators could express in no other way." Jacobson's premisses are atheistic and materialist. He is perfectly entitled to adopt this philosophical position, but two things must be said about it in the present context; (1) when applied to a discourse posited on the existence of God it will inevitably have a reductive and negative effect on interpretation; (2) it is just as much an assertion, and just as impossible to prove, as its opposite.

There is, however, a third position which Dan Jacobson does not seem to allow for, and that is agnosticism. To acknowledge that religious concepts and propositions are not susceptible of scientific verification or falsification does not necessarily entail dismissing their claims to truth and value. Agnosticism maintains (or may choose to do so) a respectful humility before the transcendental world whose existence it doubts, and therefore provides a more constructive frame of mind than atheism in which to approach the Scriptures (I think, for instance, of Frank Kermode's *The Genesis of Secrecy*). And I would venture to suggest that if belief itself, whether Jewish or Christian, Muslim or Marxist, does not have within it an element of agnosticism, the end result is likely to be fanaticism and intolerance.

Dan Jacobson's opposition between atheism and religious belief, with nothing in between, is paralleled by an equally exclusive generic opposition implied in his book between history (which is plotless and established by a positivist science) and "story" (which is fictitious and the displaced expression of human desire and anxiety). Modern literary theory, however, has tended to see these ways of representing human action as two ends of the same continuum, with many gradations in between, rather than mutually exclusive and irreconcilable discourses. And one of the key points made by Alter is that the Old Testament narratives are a complex interweaving of fiction and history. He acknowledges, here, a debt to Herbert Schneider's *Sacred Discontent* (1977), which speaks of the Bible as "historicized prose fiction", and contrasts its essentially linear, causal, prosaic account of the history of the Israelites with the cyclical, analogical, mythopoeic character of most comparable writings of the ancient world – a view aphoristically summarized in the Jakobsonian (not Jacobsonian) formula: "Where myth is hypotactic metaphors, the Bible is paratactic metonymies."

Dan Jacobson, who is arguing precisely the opposite case – that the Old Testament constitutes a total "myth" – would no doubt retort that the prophetic books are saturated with metaphor. And so they are. When one turns to the *narrative* passages of the Old Testament, however, Schneider's typification is more obviously persuasive. The description of Zedekiah's punishment is a good example: "They slew the sons of Zedekiah before his eyes, and put out the eyes of Zedekiah . . ." The lines have what Dan Jacobson rightly describes as "a certain punning quality". The first occurrence of *eyes* is a metonymy (the organ of sight standing for the faculty of sight), the second is literal; and it is the paratactic syntax (linking two grammatically equivalent clauses together by the conjunction "and" instead of subordinating one to the other in a hypotactic structure) that makes us apprehend the connection between the two with a sickening force. Heightened expression is achieved without disrupting spatio-temporal continuity.

Alter is not a structuralist, and is somewhat suspicious of Schneider's schematic formula. But he certainly thinks it is pointing in the right direction. It is, he says, "peculiar, and culturally significant that among ancient peoples only Israel should have chosen to cast its sacred national traditions in prose", and he agrees that the Old Testament is character-ized by a complex fusion of fiction and history.

> Under scrutiny, bibilical narrative generally proves to be either fiction laying claim to a place in the chain of causation and the realm of moral consequentiality that belongs to history, as in the primeval history, the tales of the Patriarchs and much of the Exodus story, and the account of the early Conquest, or history given the imaginative definition of fiction, as in most of the narratives from the period of Judges onward.

It was precisely this fusion of historical verisimilitude with the psychological interiority and thematic patterning licensed by fiction that made the novel the dominant literary mode of the modern era. "The biblical authors were among the pioneers of prose fiction in the Western tradition," Robert Alter claims, and in his explications they often seem very modern indeed – as alive to the possibilities of "spatial form" as Flaubert, as cunning in the manipulation of "point of view" as Henry James, as adept in the strategies of the "non-fiction novel" as Mailer or Capote. Applying a sophisticated critical sense sharpened on such literature, Alter finds expressive subtleties where conventional biblical scholarship finds only cruces.

Take, for example, the story about Judah, the brother of Joseph, and his daughter-in-law, Tamar, which is interpolated in the middle of the story of Joseph himself, just after he is sold into slavery. This describes how the twice-widowed Tamar is denied by Judah her right to marry his third and youngest son, but gets satisfaction by posing as a prostitute and getting herself pregnant by Judah himself (thus bearing twins, one of whom will be the progenitor of David). Biblical commentators have been able to see no point in the embedding of this story in the middle of the Joseph story, but Alter demonstrates elegantly how one story mirrors the other, the deceiver Judah (who connived at the deception of Jacob regarding the fate of Joseph) being himself deceived, and his acknowledgment of this piece of poetic justice being forced upon him by a *recognition* of his own seal, cord and staff, which Tamar had extracted from him as a pledge of payment for her sexual services, just as the deception of his father was brought about by inviting him to *recognize* (the same verb is used in both stories) the bloodied coat of Joseph.

One of Alter's most interesting insights is that the Old Testament writers allowed a considerable degree of indeterminacy into their stories by the way they chose to tell them. They were more like modern novelists than the classic novelists of the nineteenth century in that they tended to give priority to the characters' speech over the narrator's speech. The narrators of the Old Testament stories are, indeed, surprisingly reticent when one considers the ostensibly didactic motivation of the whole discourse. The more the characters are allowed to speak for themselves in a narrative text, and the less they are judged and explained by an authoritative narrator, the stronger will be our sense of their individual freedom of choice – and our own interpretative freedom. Alter finds many examples of the effectiveness of a reticent narrator in the story of David. When David leads the Ark back to Jerusalem the event is narrated from the perspective of his first wife, Michal (Samuel 2:6).

> As the Ark of the Lord came into the City of David, Michal the daughter of Saul looked out of the window and saw King David leaping and cavorting before the Lord, and she despised him in her heart.

By not explaining Michal's scorn, the narrator leaves the reader with several possible motivations:

> the undignified public spectacle which David is just now making of himself; Michal's jealousy over the moment of glory David is enjoying while she sits alone, a neglected co-wife back at the provisional palace; Michal's resentment over David's indifference to her all these years, over the other wives he has taken, over being torn away from the devoted Palti; David's dynastic ambitions – now clearly revealed in his establishing the Ark in the "City of David" – which will inevitably displace the house of Saul.

Her reaction is, in Freudian terminology, "overdetermined", as is the highly dramatic confrontation between husband and wife that immediately follows, and the stark conclusion of Michal's story, "And Michal the daughter of Saul had no child till her dying day," which could be interpreted either as a punishment for her presumption or "the last painful twist of a wronged woman's fate."

Jacobson is not, of course, ignorant of the narrative interest and psychological complexity of the Old Testament stories, as his own version of one of them, *The Rape of Tamar*, clearly shows. Admitting that, in concentrating on the story of the stories, he has done less than justice to the latter, he remarks that "they sustain this myth in many ways, not least by striving constantly, if never wholly successfully, to escape from it." This interesting observation is echoed, in a more positive form, by Alter, who argues that

> causation in human affairs itself is brought into a paradoxical double focus by the narrative techniques of the Bible. The biblical writers obviously exhibit, on the one hand, a profound belief in a strong, clearly demarcated pattern of causation in history and individual lives, and many of the framing devices, the motif-structures, the symmetries and recurrences in their narratives reflect this belief. God directs, history complies; a person sins, a person suffers; Israel backslides, Israel falls. The very perception, on the other hand, of godlike depths, unsoundable capacities for good and evil, in human nature, also leads these writers to render their protagonists in ways that destabilize any monolithic system of causation, some of them complementary or mutually reinforcing, others even mutually contradictory.

I am not suggesting that here we have a simple answer to the questions raised by Jacobson. Both books have a built-in bias. If Jacobson's is a somewhat blinkered positivism, which can see no gradations between fact and fiction, Alter's is perhaps the complacency to which all of us who practise explicatory literary criticism are prone – the assumption that when we have demonstrated pattern, coherence, richness of meaning in a text, we have done all that needs to be done, and somehow rendered it incapable of doing harm in the world. The idea of the Chosen People, whether Jewish or Christian or other, *is* a difficult and dangerous concept, whose historical consequences have been on the whole pretty disastrous. Robert Alter contributes nothing to the understanding of this particular problem because he does not address himself directly to it. What he does show, and what Dan Jacobson half-concedes in the remark quoted above, is that to detach the overarching story of the Chosen People from the innumerable stories in which it is set against the complex and unpredictable play of individual choice and fortune, is to misrepresent the Bible and what it contributes to the sum of human wisdom.

Robertson Davies and the
Campus Novel (1982)

Robertson Davies has had a long and distinguished career, not only as a novelist, but also as theatrical director, playwright and academic. He is one of Canada's most distinguished men of letters, but I have to confess that the novel under review* is my first acquaintance with his writing. Since I am unable to place it in relation to his other work, I will place it in the context of the genre, or subgenre, to which it belongs, namely, the campus novel.

This is by now a form of fiction so well established that addicts of the campus novel, like addicts of detective stories and spy thrillers, relish its familiar and recurrent features almost as much as they enjoy whatever new twist or texture the novelist is able to impart. What are the sources of the campus novel's attraction, for both readers and writers? One reason, perhaps, is that the university is a kind of microcosm of society at large, in which the principles, drives and conflicts that govern collective human life are displayed and may be studied in a clear light and on a manageable scale. One of Mr Davies's characters is of this opinion:

> The University is such a splendid community, you know, every kind of creature here, and all exhibiting what they are so much more freely than if they were in business, or the law, or whatever.

Freely, presumably, because of the institution of academic tenure, which makes scholars less afraid of their peers and superiors than members of other professions, and therefore less conformist. Universities are notoriously rich in extravagantly eccentric characters – especially in

*R. Davies, *The Rebel Angels* (Viking, 1982).

Britain (where, significantly, tenure is much more easily and quickly obtained than in the United States) and, if *The Rebel Angels* is any guide, in Canada too. Stuart Sutherland, professor of experimental psychology at the University of Sussex, England, who wrote a courageous book about his own mental illness, *Breakdown* (1976), observed that in any other social context people would have recognized much sooner that he was going mad (he had reached the stage of saving time by shaving while driving to work and dictating letters through the door of the toilet) but that in a university his symptoms were tolerantly regarded as mere eccentricities.

Inside, as outside, the academy, the principal determinants of action are sex and the will to power, and a typology of campus fiction might be based on a consideration of the relative dominance of these two drives in the story. The Cambridge novels of C. P. Snow, for instance, notably his classic study of a college election in *The Masters*, were primarily concerned with the struggle for power; while the novels of Alison Lurie, *Love and Friendship* and *The War Between the Tates*, are primarily concerned with sexual intrigue. Both themes have an essentially ironic tendency in the context of a university, whose members are supposedly dedicated to the disinterested pursuit of knowledge and truth, but who are thus revealed as slaves to ignoble instincts and passions. Sometimes the two drives are evenly balanced, as in Malcolm Bradbury's *The History Man*, whose anti-hero uses sexual seduction as a primary means of imposing his will on campus politics. More often, sexuality is opposed to the scholar's professional life, and threatens its stability. An affair between teacher and pupil, for instance, even in today's permissive society, violates some deep-seated taboo and thrusts both parties into a realm of moral danger, excitement and deception, generating the stuff of fiction. "We all know what happens in universities," says another character in *The Rebel Angels*. "Nice girls turn up, professors are human, and bingo! Sometimes it's rough on the girl, sometimes it may be destructive to the professor."

Should we perhaps rather say, "Professors would like to convince themselves that they are human"? The successful academic has usually succeeded by dint of sacrificing a certain amount of libido in youth, and in middle age may feel a sudden urge to make up for lost time, to prove that he is not a totally cerebral being after all, but a man of passion and feeling; while the young student who offers a convenient focus for the desire may be unable to disentangle sexual attraction from intellectual awe.

The exercise of power in academic life was classically analysed by F. M. Cornford in his little pamphlet *Microcosmographia Academica: being a guide for the young academic politician* (1912), which includes such gems of definition as " 'sound scholar' is a term of praise applied to one another by learned men who have no reputation outside the University" and "a lecturer is a sound scholar who is chosen to teach on the grounds that he was once able to learn." According to Cornford, the academic exercise of power consists almost as much in exploiting the democratic system of university government to frustrate others as in advancing oneself. Things have changed a bit since Cornford's Cambridge days, but it is still true that to the worldly eye the issues which preoccupy academics often seem comically disproportionate to the passions they arouse. And here we perhaps approach the ultimate secret of the campus novel's deep appeal: academic conflicts are relatively harmless, safely insulated from the real world and its sombre concerns – or capable of transforming those concerns into a form of stylized play. Essentially the campus novel is a modern, displaced form of pastoral, as Mary McCarthy recognized by calling her classic contribution to the genre *The Groves of Academe*. That is why it belongs to the literature of escape, and why we never tire of it.

The Rebel Angels is certainly a novel whose characters scarcely seem to belong to the modern world, even the modern university world; but the fact that it is a campus novel makes us readier to accept and enjoy its mannered style and archaic atmosphere. It is set in one of the constituent colleges of the University of Toronto, an institution that Mr Davies knows well, since he recently retired as master of Massey College there. But I find it hard to believe that academic life at Toronto in the 1980s can resemble Cornford's Cambridge quite as closely, or that the preoccupations of its members are quite as bizarre, as the novel suggests. *The Rebel Angels* reads like the result of an unlikely collaboration between C. P. Snow and Muriel Spark, with assistance from Thomas Love Peacock and the author of *The Anatomy of Melancholy*. Snow's relish for the cosy intrigues of academic politics is combined with Muriel Spark's zany supernaturalism, Peacock's love of good talk, and Burton's sardonic delight in esoteric learning and human eccentricity.

The novel begins well, quickly introducing the sexual theme. The narrator, a young research student of Polish-Hungarian gypsy background who rejoices in the name of Maria Magdalena Theotoky, is hurrying to see her supervisor, Clement Hollier, at the beginning of the academic year, and hears a report being passed from mouth to mouth that "Parlabane is back."

This was what I wanted. It was something to say to Hollier when we met after nearly four months apart. At that meeting he had become my lover, or so I was vain enough to think. Certainly he had become,

agonizingly, the man I loved. All through the summer vacation I had
fretted and fussed and hoped for a postcard from wherever he might
be in Europe, but he was not a man to write postcards. Not a man to
say very much, either, in a personal way. But he could be excited; he
could give way to feeling. On that day in early May, when he had told
me about the latest development in his work, and I – so eager to serve
him, to gain his gratitude and perhaps even his love – did an
inexcusable thing and betrayed the secret of the *bomari* to him, he
seemed lifted quite outside of himself, and it was then he took me in
his arms and put me on that horrible old sofa in his office, and had me
amid a great deal of confusion of clothing, creaking of springs and
peripheral anxiety lest somebody should come in. That was when we
had parted, he embarrassed and I overcome with astonishment and
devotion, and now I was to face him again. I needed an opening
remark.

The reader would be correct in inferring from this passage that Hollier is
an essentially frigid man whose only passion is his subject – "paleo-
psychology", or the investigation of popular thought and belief in the
early Renaissance period. The professor who falls genuinely in love with
Maria is Simon Darcourt, clergyman and biblical scholar, who fancies
himself as a new John Aubrey, memorializing the eccentrics of Toronto
University in a contemporary *Brief Lives*. His narrative and Maria's are
plaited together to form the substance of *The Rebel Angels*, often
covering the same event from ironically different perspectives.

Hollier and Darcourt are nominated along with Urquhart McVarish,
a historian who claims descent from the seventeeth-century translator of
Rabelais, as executors of the will of a great collector, Francis Cornish,
who has just died. Among his precious *objets d'art* and rare manuscripts
there was a hitherto unknown group of holograph letters from Rabelais
to the Renaissance magus, Paracelsus. Hollier is dying to get his hands
on these letters, partly to assuage his guilt about the seduction of Maria
by giving her the task and academic glory of editing them. But Urky
McVarish, a crotchety and malicious character, has snaffled this prize
without admitting that he has done so, much to Hollier's anger and
frustration.

The mysterious *bomari* referred to on the first page, quoted above,
turns out to be a container filled with high-grade horse dung – a
treatment to restore purity of tone to old violins, used by Maria's gypsy
mother. Introduced to "Marmusia" to learn this secret, Hollier also has
his fortune told with ominous results, while Marmusia, seeking to
secure his love for her daughter by means of a philtre, succeeds only in
binding Darcourt's affections more tightly to her.

The character who precipitates the denouement is Parlabane, a reprobate with a great scholarly future behind him, who, after many sordid and shady adventures, has come back to Toronto to batten on his old friends, Hollier and Darcourt. He is a sinister figure, often compared to the devil, who finally brings about the restoration of the Rabelais letters in a bizarre climax which it would be unfair to reveal here.

The names of Rabelais and Paracelsus are not gratuitously invoked by the plot. There is a Rabelaisian quality, a combination of robust humour and satire on pedantry, in Mr Davies's own writing; while the hermetic and heterodox ideas associated with the name of Paracelsus are exploited in a fashion that is at once playful and serious. The mythology of Gnosticism runs through the novel and explains its title. Maria Theotoky, whose name means "bringer of God", is worshipped by Darcourt as "Sophia", the feminine personification of Divine Wisdom, while she identifies him and Hollier as Samahazai and Azazel, two rebel angels in apocryphal scripture who

> came down to earth and taught tongues, and healing and laws and hygiene – taught everything – and they were often special successes with "the daughters of men" . . . Surely it is the explanation of the origin of universities!

The Rebel Angels is one of those novels that impart a good deal of information – in this case rather esoteric information – as well as entertainment to the reader. Its flavour will be a little too gamy for some tastes, its high spirits too redolent of high table; but as the production of a writer in his sixty-ninth year, it is a work of impressive vigour and vivacity, which no addict of the campus novel will want to miss.

Life Between Covers (1984)

Anything a writer does after winning the Nobel Prize is apt to seem an anticlimax. William Golding's new novel, *The Paper Men*,* is no exception to the rule. Its reception by reviewers in Britain has been what is euphemistically called "mixed" – in other words, respectfully disappointed. I was disappointed myself on first acquaintance, but thought better of it on a second reading. It is not quite the novel it appears to be – or, to be more precise, it is not a good example of the kind of novel it appears to be: a comedy of literary and academic manners. But it is an interesting variation on a kind of novel that Mr Golding has made peculiarly his own – the fable of spiritual crisis.

The narrator, Wilfred Barclay, is a British novelist of some literary reputation, who bears a teasing resemblance to Golding himself (bearded, dishevelled, with a home in the West Country) though he is somewhat younger and very much less respectable than his creator. The story chiefly concerns Barclay's fraught relationship with an American academic, Rick L. Tucker, who has made the novelist his special study, is anxious to become his biographer and literary executor, and will not take no for an answer. The tale begins on a note of excellent farce, with the American professor caught going through the domestic trash cans of his host, the novelist, in the middle of the night, in search of manuscript material. Barclay, mistaking the researcher for a badger, wings him with an air-gun pellet as his own insecurely fastened pyjama trousers subside around his ankles.

This ludicrous episode inadvertently reveals to Barclay's wife, Elizabeth, some previously concealed infidelity, and breaks up their already fragile marriage. Barclay seeks to escape his problems – and his aspirant biographer – by taking to the freeways and airways of the

* W. Golding, *The Paper Men* (Viking, New York, 1984).

world, moving from place to place in a haze of alcohol and repressed guilt. But Rick L. Tucker catches up with him some years later in a hotel high above Lake Zurich, pesters him tirelessly to be appointed his official biographer, seems to offer his own new, young, and beautiful bride's sexual favours as a bribe, and then, to the novelist's chagrin, saves the latter's life when a handrail on the edge of a yawning chasm suddenly gives way in the fog. The deed is less heroic than it seems, but Barclay doesn't know this, and seeks to escape his indebtedness by absconding again, in a series of planes and hired cars, leaving a trail of false forwarding addresses behind him like a criminal on the run.

Clearly there is promising material for fiction here. The relationship between biographer and biographee (to coin a necessary term) is full of human and dramatic interest, especially when the latter is still living. Even when the work has been authorized, there is apt to be some tension between the two parties involved, for the biographer will naturally want to probe into just those areas of the subject's life that he or she would prefer to keep concealed from public scrutiny – either because they are shameful or because (if the biographee is a writer) they may encourage a reductive interpretation of the imaginative work.

The literary biographer is an empirical researcher, a kind of historian; he is bound by his discipline to pursue the facts into the deepest recesses of his subject's personal life and psyche. He is willy-nilly a textual sleuth, for whom works of fiction are mysteries to be solved, by following a trail of clues back into the writer's experience. When a novel, play, or poem is traced to its "source" in the writer's life, however, there is some danger that the larger public significance of the former may be displaced by the fascinating empirical reality of the latter. Not surprisingly, therefore, writers seldom authorize biographies of themselves while they are still alive, and often leave widows staunchly defending their privacy when they are dead.

At this very moment a controversy is raging, mainly in the correspondence pages of *The Times Literary Supplement,* about access to the manuscript sources for the life of T. S. Eliot. The controversy has been triggered by a new play, called *Tom and Viv,* by Michael Hastings, which explores the tormented relationship between the poet and his first wife, and suggests that he took the initiative in having her certified insane. Hastings has defended the speculative nature of his play by accusing the executrix of the Eliot estate, Mrs Valerie Eliot (his second wife), of obstructing access to her husband's private papers. Mrs Eliot has denied the charge. Other correspondents have argued fiercely about the ethical and critical issues involved in the dispute. Do we have any right to know the painful details of Eliot's marital problems just because he is famous and dead? Is such information necessary or even relevant to a proper reading of his poetry?

These are fascinating and intricate questions. No doubt our answers will depend in part on the character of the writer involved, and in part on the tact of the biographical researcher. Eliot's poetry is so fragile, precariously poised between the artfully allusive and the enigmatically subjective, that its subtle suggestiveness could easily be destroyed by the heavy hand of biographical interpretation. But the artistic reputation of James Joyce has been enhanced rather than demeaned by the meticulous scholarship of Richard Ellmann, and the initial shock of reading Joyce's polymorphously perverse erotic letters to Nora soon wears off and does not affect the fundamental humour and compassion of his treatment of human sexuality in *Ulysses* and *Finnegans Wake*.

Joyce's friend and amanuensis, Samuel Beckett, has always had the reputation of being one of the most intensely private and reclusive of modern writers; so there was considerable astonishment (and not a little envy) in the literary world when a totally unknown young American academic, Deirdre Bair, published a major biography in 1978, full of startling, well-documented revelations about Beckett's early life. In her preface she explains that when she first approached Beckett about the project, as a doctoral candidate in search of a dissertation topic, he told her that he would neither help nor hinder her. She took this as a kind of permission, though admits that "I am sure he did not want this book to be written, and would have been grateful if I had abandoned it." Bair's biggest single coup was discovering and getting access to a cache of letters written by Beckett to his friend Thomas McGreevy. "So you've found them, then," Beckett commented stoically, like the culprit on the last page of a detective story holding out his wrists for the handcuffs. He seems to have agreed to play the part of the hunted rodent in the biographical game of cat-and-mouse out of courtesy or apathy. Or was he, as Bair suggests, intrigued, in spite of himself, at the opportunity to see "in his own lifetime how posterity would view him"?

Something of the same equivocation is admitted by Golding's fictitious novelist. "I feared to be the object of a biography. At the same time I was – no matter how hard I tried not to be – I was flattered by the possibility." But the grave, enigmatic courtesy of Samuel Beckett's dealings with Deirdre Bair is very different from the paranoid flight of Wilfred Barclay from Rick L. Tucker's "sedulous search into a past raw with unforgiving memories". In making his author a somewhat eccentric and wayward Englishman and his biographer a stolid, humourless American academic, Golding has set up a situation that is full of dramatic potential, and not without parallels in the real world of contemporary letters. Though Golding knows very well – who better? – what it is like to be a writer from whose imagination numerous professional scholars derive a parasitic living, he does not seem to know either the academic world or Americans well enough to make his novel work as literary satire.

It is impossible to get the character of Tucker into focus, or to place him in any recognizable academic context. Barclay surprises his aspirant biographer at an academic conference giving a paper on his use of relative clauses ("He had counted them, apparently, book by book. He had made a graph . . ."). Yet this kind of stylistic criticism is rarely if ever practised by literary biographers. Then it turns out that Tucker first introduced himself to Barclay under false pretences, as an assistant professor, when he was really just a research student; then, that he is being sponsored by a fabulously rich American collector of literary manuscripts who has given him seven years to get his hands on the Barclay archive, a deadline Tucker is desperate to meet. This melo-dramatic plotting (it entails Tucker's wife, Mary Lou, who becomes the millionaire's mistress) seems quite unnecessary to motivate the biographer: the desire to get tenure at the University of Astrakhan, Nebraska, would do just as well and be more plausible.

There are other improbabilities: Tucker speaks of getting his "dee phil", and wears a shirt of broad brown and white stripes – both British rather than American characteristics. There is some rather facile ridiculing of American idiom in the small-talk of Tucker and his bride ("'Was there any sun, hon?' . . . 'Why none, hon . . .'"). But most importantly, and damagingly, Tucker never displays that obsessive inwardness with his subject's work that is the characteristic mark of the really dedicated biographical critic, and which writers tend to find disconcerting rather than flattering. Rick Tucker never utters a line that suggests he could have written a good undergraduate paper on the work of Wilfred Barclay, let alone a critical biography. Instead he says things like, "You are part of the Great Pageant of English Literature."

If we suspend our disbelief in this level of the story, however, there is much to enjoy and ponder in *The Paper Men*. The title, consciously or unconsciously, echoes T. S. Eliot's "The Hollow Men". Both Barclay and Tucker are "paper men" not only in the metonymic sense that they live off and by paper (in the form of books, manuscripts, letters, etc.) but also in the metaphorical sense of being two-dimensional, incomplete human beings. Barclay has done more violence to his own self than any inquisitive biographer could do, by a lifetime's indulgence in vanity, lust, and booze, and he has injured his wife and daughter in the process. Tucker has sacrificed his own integrity as a human being in the unscrupulous quest to possess another's secrets. Both become equally paranoid and begin to hallucinate sightings of each other in different parts of the world. Their symbiotic relationship becomes crazier and crazier, climaxing in a blackly comic scene of ritual humiliation, when Barclay forces Tucker to lap white wine, doggie-fashion, from a saucer, as the price of becoming his executor.

This nasty deed, equally degrading to both parties, is in fact Barclay's last desperate effort to resist the force of a religious illumination which has come to him unbidden and unexpected in the course of his travels, when he confronts a statue of Christ in a Sicilian cathedral.

> It was taller than I am, broad-shouldered and striding forward like an archaic Greek statue. It was crowned and its eyes were rubies or garnets or carbuncles or plain red glass that flared like the heat in my chest . . . I stood there with my mouth open and the flesh crawling over my body. I knew in one destroying instant that all my adult life I had believed in God and this knowledge was a vision of God. Fright entered the very marrow of my bones. Surrounded, swamped, confounded, all but destroyed, adrift in the universal intolerance, mouth open, screaming, bepissed and beshitten, I knew my maker and I fell down.

Wilfred Barclay thus joins the company of other, earlier Golding protagonists, like Pincher Martin, Sammy Mountjoy in *Free Fall*, and Dean Jocelin in *The Spire*, characters whose egotism and self-sufficiency collapse under the implacable pressure of the God whom they had denied or defied. Golding actually uses the same crustacean imagery for Barclay as for Pincher Martin. A "camp" friend tells him,

> "You see you are what biologists used to call exoskeletal. Most people are what they called endoskeletal, have their bones inside. But you my dear, for some reason known only to God, as they say of anonymous bodies, have spent your life inventing a skeleton on the outside. Like crabs and lobsters. That's terrible you see, because the worms get inside and, oh my aunt Jemima, they have the place to themselves. So my advice . . . is to get rid of armour, the exoskeleton, the carapace, before it's too late."

Golding's religious vision is powerful and idiosyncratic, deeply Protestant (or Pauline) in its emphasis on "conversion", and yet suffused with a Catholic mysticism. Wilfred Barclay finds himself suffering the stigmata – pains in the hands and feet corresponding to the wounds of the crucified Christ, "like St Francis in reverse, as it were, for being a mother-fucking bastard as my best friend would say, instead of getting them as a prize for being good". Since Barclay is an alcoholic, and by his own admission "very receptive to hypnotic suggestion", the secular reader is free to interpret all this supernaturalism as psychosomatic, but it does change Wilfred Barclay's character. Whether the change comes "too late", as his friend warns him, is a moot point. Too late to offer comfort to his ailing wife, certainly, and too late to win back the love of his alienated daughter, but not perhaps too late to regain his own soul. Mr Golding's novels are famous for their last-minute reversals of plot or implication. This time he has delayed the effect till the very last word of his text – and it is a stunner. To reveal more would be a sin against fiction.

The Art of Ring Lardner (1984)

The most obvious recommendation of Ring Lardner is that he is a very funny writer. Humour is the most ephemeral of all literary qualities, but Lardner, at his very best, belongs to that select company of writers who can make posterity lift its head from the page and laugh aloud. But he is not just a humorist. His stories constitute a fascinating and illuminating record of a certain phase of American social history – the teens and twenties of the present century, when America was coming of age as a major modern power, with all the awkwardness, ebullience and occasional dissipation of a young man reaching his majority. It was a time of restless social mobility, of fortunes made and lost in a rapidly expanding capitalist economy, of conspicious consumption and dismal poverty, of struggle between the traditional values of small towns and agrarian communities and the more sophisticated and cynical life-styles of big cities like New York and Chicago. It was a period that saw the advent of commercialized spectator sport, mass-circulation newspapers and magazines, jazz-based popular music, Prohibition and speakeasies. The Ring Lardner stories are vivid verbal snapshots of that America: baseball players and commercial travellers, Broadway impresarios and small-town barbers, flappers and gold-diggers, are preserved in these pages, luminously lifelike but bathed in a sepia tint of yesteryear.

In spite of the United States' involvement in the Great War, and thus in world politics, Europe was still a week's voyage away, and for most Americans infinitely more distant in psychological and cultural terms. America remained in many ways a very provincial, inward-looking society – naive, philistine and materialistic. Many American writers – T. S. Eliot, Ezra Pound, Gertrude Stein, Ernest Hemingway, for instance – found it inhospitable to literary art, and settled or travelled extensively in Europe. Ring Lardner made few trips to Europe and these left very little mark on his writing. In terms of Philip Rahv's celebrated division of American writers into Palefaces (those oriented to the European and specifically English literary tradition) and Redskins (those trying to create a distinctively American literature "on native ground") Lardner is definitely a Redskin. But he was an urban, or suburban, Redskin. He did not yearn nostalgically for the frontier and the wilderness, from which Redskin writing derives its positive values and mythopoeic inspiration. He moved almost exclusively in those areas of his native land already thoroughly tamed and domesticated by the railroad and the motor car. Perhaps for that reason, his picture of his society is sardonic and far from flattering. His perspective may have been narrow, compared to that of his expatriate contemporaries, but it was clear-sighted and critical. Beneath the humour of these stories there is sometimes detectable an almost Swiftian misanthropy. This puzzled many who knew him personally. As Elizabeth Hardwick has succinctly put it: "He came from a charming, talented family and married a woman he loved. He was kind, reserved, hardworking; his fictional world is loud, cruel, filled with desperate marriages, hideous old age, suburban wretchedness, fraud, drunkenness." Ring Lardner himself, however, was given to sporadic bouts of self-destructive drinking, in which, if we need it, we can find some biographical clue to the dark side of his literary imagination.

Ringgold Wilmer Lardner – to unfurl in its full splendour a name he was glad to conceal behind the homely abbreviation "Ring" – was born in 1885, in the small Midwestern town of Niles, Michigan. His father owned a prosperous farming business, and Ring enjoyed a comfortable, almost idyllic upbringing, until, in his teens, the family fortunes suffered a reverse, which, among other consequences, prevented him from proceeding to college. After an abortive attempt to make a mechanical engineer out of him ("I can't think of no walk in life for which I had more of a natural bent," he remarked later, "unless it would be hostess at a roller rink") Ring became a sports journalist on a local paper, and showed such aptitude, especially as a baseball reporter, that he swiftly graduated to the big newspapers of Chicago and the East Coast. He wrote a daily baseball column for five years between 1908 and 1913, and continued to cover big games until the early '20s, though he became somewhat disillusioned with the sport after the so-called Black Sox scandal of 1919, when the Chicago White Sox conspired with a betting syndicate to "throw" the World Series. The incident has been immortalized in a reference in *The Great Gatsby* by Scott Fitzgerald, who undoubtedly discussed it privately with Lardner. In 1922 Fitzgerald and Zelda moved to the fashionable community of Great Neck, Long Island (the original of East Egg and West Egg in *The Great Gatsby*), where Ring Lardner had a house, and the two men became friends.

By this time Lardner had more or less abandoned sports journalism, and was a successful freelance writer of humorous columns and short stories. This was a period when magazines such as the *Saturday Evening Post* occupied much the same position in popular culture as TV does today: they commanded huge national audiences and could pay immense sums to writers like Ring Lardner who enjoyed a strong personal following. In his heyday, Ring Lardner was among the highest-paid writers in America. In 1927 *Cosmopolitan* (not to be confused with the present-day bearer of that name) was paying him $4,500 for a single story (a sum equivalent to $25,000 in today's currency). Though he wrote for the same lucrative market, Scott Fitzgerald had his eyes fixed on literary immortality, and was continually badgering his friend to adopt a more serious attitude to the art of letters. Fitzgerald introduced Lardner to his editor, the famous Maxwell Perkins, at Scribner's, who then became the publishers of his short fiction, but together they never succeeded in persuading him to write a novel, or, for that matter, to put his stories before the public with the dignity appropriate to a modern literary master. His first collection for Scribner's was prefaced by a spoof introduction entitled "How To Write Short Stories", and each item was prefaced with a surrealistically misleading synopsis. For example, a baseball yarn is described as "The love story, half earthly, half spiritual, of a beautiful snare drummer and a hospital interne, unique for its word pictures of the unpleasant after-effects of anaesthesia. It explains what radio is and how it works."

Something of Scott Fitzgerald's exasperation at Lardner's refusal to take his vocation with a high modern seriousness came out in his obituary on Lardner's death in 1933 (a premature one, brought on by TB and excessive drinking). "Whatever Ring's achievement was it fell short of the achievement he was capable of, and this because of a cynical attitude towards his work." Fitzgerald traced this back to Ring Lardner's youthful infatuation with baseball.

> During those years, when most men of promise achieve an adult education, if only in the school of war, Ring moved in the company of a few dozen illiterates playing a boy's game. A boy's game, with no more possibilities in it than a boy could master, a game bounded by walls which kept out novelty or danger, change or adventure.

There is perhaps some truth in this harsh judgement, but there is also the paradox that it was through baseball that Ring Lardner found his voice (or rather, voices) as a creative writer, and thus made his distinctive contribution to modern American fiction – the development of a vernacular literary style. The process has been well documented by his most recent biographer, Jonathan Yardley (*Ring: A Biography of Ring Lardner*, New York, 1977).

When Ring Lardner was travelling around the country with the Chicago Cubs in 1910–11 he began to use in his daily column (which had to be filled whether there was a game to report or not) the quoted comments of one of the players, Frank Schulte. Schulte had a sardonic wit that was akin to Lardner's own, and was often exercised at the expense of his team mates:

> "They didn't trip us today because they played better ball. Oh no . . . You saw Jack Murray hit that one out of the ballyard? Well, that's no credit to Murray. He had his eyes shut or was talking to someone back in the grandstand when he let that one loose. He didn't meet the ball square. Oh no. The ball hit his little finger nail and bounded off it over the fence."

How much of this is quotation, and how much Lardner's invention, we shall never know; but, as Yardley observes, we can see here the first burgeoning of the style of mature baseball stories like "Alibi Ike", in which a richly resourceful vernacular rhetoric expresses and exposes human vanity, folly and pretence in a way that is both specific to the small, self-obsessed world of baseball and yet universally recognizable. The actual transition from sports journalism to prose fiction was made in 1916, with "A Bushman's Letters Home", a series of letters ostensibly written by a brash and barely literate rookie, trying to make it in big-league baseball, to his friend back home in Bedford, Indiana. These pieces were collected and published, with considerable success, under the title *You Know Me Al*.

That title illustrates and encapsulates Ring Lardner's mastery of the vernacular style. The absence of the comma that would be conventional in written English after "Me" compels the reader to punctuate the phrase himself in order to interpret it – thus compels him to pronounce it silently to himself, hearing its rhythm and intonation, recognizing and relishing its rhetorical function, at once phatic and self-congratulatory. Virginia Woolf paid a surprising but characteristically acute tribute to the achievement:

> With extraordinary ease and aptitude, with the quickest strokes, the surest touch, the sharpest insight, he lets Jack Keefe the baseball player cut out his own outline, fill in his own depths, until the figure of the foolish, boastful, innocent athlete lives before us.

She also provided (in advance, for she was writing in *The Dial* in 1925) a riposte to Scott Fitzgerald's obituary criticism:

> It is no coincidence that the best of Mr Lardner's stories are about games, for one may guess that Mr Lardner's interest in games has solved one of the most difficult problems of the American writer; it has given him a clue, a centre, a meeting place for the divers activities of people whom a vast continent isolates, whom no tradition controls. Games give him what society gives his English brother.

In fact not all Ring Lardner's best stories are about games, and some of them are about social manners (for example, "Ex Parte" and "Mr and Mrs Fixit"), but most of them are cast in the form of monologues, letters or journals, uttered or written in the American vernacular by invented characters, and this was a mode of writing that Ring Lardner discovered through baseball. In order to explain the importance of this discovery, it is necessary to indulge in a little literary history, and even literary theory – doing our best to ignore the derisive shade of Ring Lardner hovering over the exercise.

A distinctive feature of the novel as a genre (some would say, its most important distinguishing feature) is that it has assimilated and combined a whole range of discourses suppressed and excluded by the decorums of classical epic and traditional romance – not only by the vivid imitation of different kinds of speech in dialogue, but by letting characters tell their own stories in their own language. The pseudo-autobiographies of Defoe, the epistolary novels of Samuel Richardson, in the eighteenth century, revolutionized narrative literature and prepared the way for more subtle and self-conscious experiments by modern novelists with unreliable narrators, streams of consciousness and interior monologues. The effect of letting the characters' distinctive voices be heard in, and on occasion take over, the narrative discourse, is not only to gain realism and immediacy, but also to "defamiliarize" the world we inhabit (thus making it more perceptible) by refusing the familiar, conventional ways of representing it in literature.

This was always a particularly urgent need for American writers, struggling to articulate the experience of a new and emergent nation in a literary language suffocated under the weight of European tradition. The great breakthrough was made by Mark Twain who, in *Huckleberry Finn* (1884), made the informal speech of an uneducated country boy a wonderfully eloquent medium through which to express profound insights into the nature of America and American society. Ernest Hemingway paid famous homage to the achievement, and acknowledged his own debt to Twain, when he declared, "All modern American literature comes from one book by Mark Twain called *Huckleberry Finn*." But, arguably, it was Ring Lardner's early stories and journalism that showed the young Hemingway how the stylistic lessons of *Huckleberry Finn* might be applied and adapted to more modern subject-matter. Charles A. Fenton records in *The Apprenticeship of Ernest Hemingway* that a teacher at his high school "was always having to fight criticism by the superintendent that Ernie was writing like Ring Lardner" in the school newspaper; and in 1932 Hemingway inscribed a copy of *Death in the Afternoon*, "To Ring Lardner, from his early imitator and always admirer." Other writers directly influenced by Lardner include Sherwood Anderson, James T. Farrell, Nathanael

West, John O'Hara, James Thurber, Damon Runyon and J. D. Salinger. There are scores of others indirectly influenced by his experiments with vernacular narrative.

In terms of literary history, Ring Lardner's example was as important as his actual achievement, and one must be careful not to exaggerate the latter. He left comparatively few stories that are indisputably first class, and these are invariably ones in which the form of vernacular narration disguises or displaces those aspects of the art of fiction in which he was weak. He was, for instance, as he readily admitted, a poor hand at constructing a plot, and tended to rely on stock formulae and melodramatic stereotypes. "Haircut", with its poetic justice for the town bully who teased the idiot boy and persecuted the innocent heroine, is an example; but we are hardly aware of the artificiality of the story because of the fascinating indirection of its telling. The town barber is regaling a customer with an admiring and nostalgic account of the bully's brutal and humourless practical jokes, and everything he says has to be interpreted in a sense opposite to what he intends. The barber's shop is a perfect setting for a dramatic monologue of which Browning himself might have been proud, for the reader is compelled to place himself, as it were, in the position of the silent listener, trapped in the chair, inwardly disgusted yet unable to stem the flow of mean-minded, bigoted, complacent, sexist garrulity.

"Champion" is another story about a bully which undoubtedly has its moments, but is less successful as a whole than "Haircut". It is no coincidence, I think, that this story is more conventional in form, narrated by an authorial voice that often sounds stilted and uneasy in contrast to the colloquial speech of the characters:

Midge, on the contrary, gave his new manager's wife the many times over, *and seemed loath to end the feast of his eyes.*

"Some doll," he said to Grace when they were alone.

"Doll is right," the lady replied, "and sawdust where her brains ought to be."

"I'm li'ble to steal that baby," said Midge, and he smiled as *he noted the effect of his words on his audience's face.* [Italics mine]

Edmund Wilson recorded a revealing conversation with Ring Lardner that took place in the Fitzgerald's house at Great Neck.

When we were talking about his own work, Lardner said that the trouble was he couldn't write straight English. I asked him what he meant and he said: "I can't write a sentence like, 'We were sitting in the Fitzgeralds' house and the fire was burning brightly.'"

What he *could* write were sentences like:

> This is our first separation since we have been engaged, nearly 17 days. It will be 17 days tomorrow. And the hotel orchestra at dinner this evening played that old thing "Oh how I miss you tonight" and it seemed as if they must be playing it for my benefit though of course the person in that song is talking about how they miss their mother though of course I miss mother too, but a person gets used to missing their mother and it isn't like Walter or the person you are engaged to. ("I Can't Breathe")

Or:

> You must write and tell me how you are getting along in the "battle of Broadway" (I laughed when I read that) and whether the publishers like your songs though I know they will. Am crazy to hear them and hear you play the piano as I love good jazz music even better than classical, though I suppose it is terrible to say such a thing. But I usually say just what I think though sometimes I wish afterwards I had not of. But I still believe it is better for a girl to be her own self and natural instead of always acting. But am afraid I will never have a chance to hear you play unless you come back to Chi and pay us a visit as my "threat" was just a "threat" and I don't see any hope of ever getting there unless some rich New Yorker should fall in love with me and take me there to live. Fine chance for poor little me, eh, Mr Lewis? ("Some Like Them Cold")

Or:

> After dinner we made them come up to our house and we all set in the parlor, which the young woman had give us the use of to entertain company. We begun talking over old times and Mother said she was a-scared Mrs Hartsell would find it tiresome listening to we three talk over old times, but as it turned out they wasn't much chance for nobody else to talk with Mrs Hartsell in the company. I have heard lots of women that could go it, but Hartsell's wife takes the cake of all the women I ever seen. She told us the family history of everybody in the State of Michigan and bragged for a half hour about her son, who she said is in the drug business in Grand Rapids, and a Rotarian. ("The Golden Honeymoon")

Ring Lardner is at his best when he allows his men and women to speak for themselves, without authorial intervention or interpretation. These characters reveal themselves – their hopes and fears and vanities and flaws – to hilarious or pitiful effect in language that is, by conventional literary standards, impoverished and imperfect, but, when subtly manipulated by the invisible Lardner, wonderfully expressive. That apparently redundant distinction in the first passage between "Walter or the person you are engaged to", for instance, is a kind of Freudian slip since, as we soon discover, the young lady in question is rather promiscuous in her engagements. Behind the arch quotation marks, the tortuous qualifications, the unsubtle flattery and self-justification of the second passage, we sense the desperate anxiety of a woman trying to attract a potential husband without violating the code of gentility to which she pretends. Through speech, or speech transcribed into writing, a character and a whole way of life are revealed to us, and the plot line is essentially a pretext for this exposure.

Perhaps the most daring, technically speaking, of the three stories cited above is "The Golden Honeymoon", which is virtually plotless. An elderly couple from New Jersey take a winter vacation in Florida in a resort filled with other old people. The husband records the trivial minutiae of the journey, the accommodation, and the banal diversions of the resort. They meet another couple, the male half of whom was an old flame of the narrator's wife, keep irritable company with them for a while, compete at various games, quarrel and fall out. The narrator and his wife are reconciled. Then they go home. Nothing is said or done that is not of the utmost banality, yet it would be hard to say whether the story redeems or exposes that banality. It is positively Chekhovian in the flawless realism of its surface and the ambiguity of its import. One may read it as either a horrifying indictment of the vacancy of old age in modern Western society, or as tender celebration of marriage as companionship. Significantly, the *Saturday Evening Post*, to whom it was first offered, turned it down because they thought it would surprise and unsettle Ring Lardner's regular readers. It is in some ways his most "modern", most experimental story.

Ring Lardner himself, as Fitzgerald discovered, had no pretensions to Parnassus. He liked to regard himself as an entertainer who wrote by instinct and from experience. "I don't worry about plots," he said once. "I just start writing about someone I think I know something about. I try to get him down cold. The other characters seem to walk into the story naturally enough. I seldom write a story of more than 5,000 words – my mind seems geared to that length. I write about 3,000 words about nothing; that is a terrible struggle. Then I come to, and say to myself, 'I must get a punch in this.' I stop and figure out the punch, then sail through to the finish." Though the tone is characteristically throwaway and self-deprecating, this is probably a reliable account of Ring Lardner's working method. And the phrase "terrible struggle", in spite of its ironical placing, gives us a glimpse of the hard work and creative concentration that must have gone into the composition of the best of his stories. Writing of that quality was never easy.

D. H. Lawrence:
Genius, Heretic, Classic (1985)

A hundred years ago – on 11 September 1885, to be precise – in the small terraced home of a coalminer, in the pit village of Eastwood, Nottinghamshire, a child was born who grew up to become one of the most celebrated of modern English writers. In the opinion of many literary critics, he was the greatest of them; and, if we interpret "English" in the narrow sense, excluding Irishmen, naturalized Americans and the odd expatriate Pole, David Herbert Lawrence's claim to that accolade would be difficult to dispute. But Lawrence being Lawrence, there will probably always be some controversy about the precise nature and status of his achievement. We may say of him, as Lionel Trilling once said of Jane Austen, that the opinions which have been held of his work are almost as interesting, and almost as important to think about, as the work itself.

To his own contemporaries he was a wayward genius. "In the early days they were always telling me I had got genius," Lawrence wryly reminisced in 1928, "as if to console me for not having their own incomparable advantages." "They" were the established figures and aristocratic patrons of the metropolitan literary world, to which Lawrence gained a rapid entrée in spite of his humble provincial background. In 1910, Jessie Chambers, with whom he had an intense and tormented quasi-platonic relationship throughout his adolescence and youth (she is portrayed as Miriam in *Sons and Lovers*), copied out some of his poems and sent them to Ford Madox Hueffer, editor of the *English Review*. Hueffer promptly published them, and, shortly afterwards, Lawrence's early short stories. Shown Lawrence's first novel, *The White Peacock*, Hueffer told him that it had every fault that the English novel could have, but added, "You've got GENIUS." It was published by Heinemann, the first publisher to see it, in 1911, and was a *succès d'estime*.

Lawrence resigned his post as teacher in a Croydon elementary school and became a full-time writer. He also fell in love and ran away with Frieda Weekley, the wife of the Professor of French at Nottingham University. Frieda, *née* von Richthofen, put him in touch with progressive central European thought, especially about sex, and helped him revise the manuscript of *Sons and Lovers* in the light of Freud, of whose Oedipus complex the autobiographical novel was a classic illustration. Though that book, published in 1912, hardly received the acclaim it deserved, it confirmed the author's promise as a major writer in the making. In short, Lawrence was launched upon his literary career with remarkable ease. It was later that he experienced almost unbearable frustration and disappointment.

A major stumbling-block was his keen interest in and (by the standards of his day) daringly explicit treatment of sexual relations. *The Rainbow*, published in 1915, was suppressed on grounds of indecency, without the publisher (Methuen) offering any defence, and was not issued again until 1926. *Women in Love*, which Lawrence finished in 1917, could not find a publisher until 1920, and then crept out in a limited edition. The suppression of these two linked novels, which he rightly considered his most ambitious and original achievement, embittered Lawrence against his native country, and contributed to his choice of exile as a way of life. As soon as the hateful Great War was over (his weak constitution exempted him from military service, but he and his German wife were continually harassed by the authorities), Lawrence and Frieda left England and commenced a nomadic life which took them to Italy, Australia, America and Mexico.

At the same period another literary exile, James Joyce, was having similar problems with censorship over *Ulysses*, but the Irishman enjoyed more unanimous respect and support from the literary avant-garde. Lawrence was a maverick modernist, always regarded with a certain uneasiness by his peers. He belonged to no literary school or clique. He did not subscribe to the orthodox modernist belief, derived from nineteenth-century Aestheticism and Symbolism, in the priority of form over content. On meeting Ezra Pound, he noted in a letter: "His god is beauty, mine life." Lawrence's literary experiments were prophetically rather than aesthetically motivated. The application of myth to modern experience, which Joyce and T. S. Eliot contrived through ironic analogy, manifested itself in Lawrence's writing as ritual *action*, rendered with disconcerting directness. Increasingly convinced that industrial civilization was in its death throes, of which the Great War was the final convulsion, he looked to pagan religions centring on blood, sun and vegetation for models of renewal. This got up the aquiline nose of T .S. Eliot, especially in his "classical, royalist and Anglo-Catholic" phase, and in *After Strange Gods* (1934) he pilloried Lawrence as a modern "heretic".

The notoriety of *Lady Chatterley's Lover*, published in Italy in 1928, which *John Bull* had "no hesitation in describing as the most evil outpouring that has ever besmirched the literature of our country", did nothing to modify the general view that Lawrence was a writer whose great artistic gifts had been spoiled by his messianic delusions and obsession with sex. When he died of tuberculosis in 1930, at the age of forty-four, leaving behind him an astonishingly abundant corpus of novels, stories, plays, poems, essays and travel books, the tone of the obituaries was generally mean and condescending, provoking E. M. Forster into a generous and dignified tribute: "Now he is dead, and the low-brows whom he scandalized have united with the high-brows whom he bored to ignore his greatness . . . All that we can do . . . is to say straight out that he was the greatest imaginative novelist of our generation."

Few people shared Forster's high valuation in 1930. One was Aldous Huxley, who edited the first selection of the five thousand letters Lawrence left behind. Another was an obscure Cambridge don called F. R. Leavis, whose championship of Lawrence was to play a major part in the later rise of Lawrence's reputation, as the *Scrutiny* school of criticism gradually extended its influence of English Studies in higher and secondary education throughout Britain and the Commonwealth.

It might be said that if Lawrence had not existed, Leavis and *Scrutiny* would have had to invent him (some would add, their Lawrence *was* an invention). The Leavisian emphasis on the moral value of literary studies required a great modern writer who would embody this redemptive cultural mission. As Leavis put it in his book, *D. H. Lawrence, Novelist* (1955), the product of more than thirty years' devoted study, "The insight, the wisdom, the revived and re-educated feeling for health, that Lawrence brings are what, as our civilization goes, we desperately need."

Leavis's reading of Lawrence stressed his critique of industrial mass society, his working-class and nonconformist roots, his concern for the quality of human life, and his effort to restore or rediscover the values of an "organic community". It ignored or underplayed some of the less obviously healthy elements in Lawrence's thought and fiction, such as his readiness to sacrifice individual human lives to Life with a capital "L" (see, for instance, the implicit endorsement of murder in "The Captain's Doll" and "The Fox", and the celebration of ritual killing in "The Woman Who Rode Away"), his sexism, and his messianic, apocalyptic mysticism, that sometimes drew him towards fascist ideological positions, and on occasion to the edge of madness.

The accusation of fascism was particularly damaging to Lawrence's reputation in the *marxisant* literary climate of the 30s. A familiar defence was that Lawrence himself finally rejected the ideology of his "leadership novels" (*Aaron's Rod, Kangaroo* and *The Plumed Serpent*) in a letter heralding *Lady Chatterley's Lover*: "The leader-cum-follower relationship is a bore. And the new relationship will be a sort of tenderness, sensitive, between men and men, men and women . . ." As Lawrence's stock soared in the 1950s, the pressure grew for an unexpurgated British edition of his last major novel, and in 1960 the prestigious house of Penguin took the responsibility and the risk.

The resulting obscenity trial at the Old Bailey was one of the turning-points of British social history. When Mr Griffith-Jones asked members of the jury, rhetorically, whether they would wish "your wife or your servants" to read *Lady Chatterley's Lover*, a great gust of derisive laughter arose from the country at large that blew away the last cobwebs of pre-war class society. When defence witness Richard Hoggart pa·ntly explained to the same counsel why the word "puritan" could legitimately be applied to Lawrence, students and teachers of Eng. Lit. everywhere rejoiced in the victory of critical discourse over legal.

After the triumphant acquittal, Warden Sparrow of All Souls stirred up more controversy by pointing out that the seventh "bout" between Lady Chatterley and her lover, though described in untypically vague language, evidently involved anal intercourse, and wondered what the expert witnesses for the defence would have said if Griffith-Jones had challenged them with this passage, instead of unaccountably reserving it for an ambiguous mention in his closing speech. One hopes that they would have been able to explain that this sexual act had a special symbolic significance for Lawrence, connected with his ideas about corruption and decay being a necessary stage in resurrection and renewal – though it was more than a decade before critics like Frank Kermode and Colin Clarke elucidated this aspect of Lawrence's "metaphysic".

In the meantime, the publication of *Lady Chatterley's Lover* gave a great impetus to the onset of the Permissive Society. The assurance of the leading defence counsel to the jury at the Old Bailey, that acquittal would not license the use of four-letter words by "any scribbler writing any kind of novel", proved manifestly false. Since the trial, any writer has been free to describe any sexual act in any kind of language short of blasphemy. Perhaps foreseeing this effect, and believing that D. H. Lawrence himself would have deplored it, Leavis declined to testify at the trial; Eliot, interestingly, offered to depose for the defence, but was not called.

In the 60s, D. H. Lawrence was adopted as a patron saint of the Counter-Culture, became a sort of posthumous honorary hippie. With the appearance of the Women's Liberation Movement in the next decade, however, he suddenly became, almost overnight, an embarrassment to with-it radicals. The crucial document here was Kate Millett's *Sexual Politics* (1970), a formidable indictment of male chauvinism in Anglo-American culture, which grouped Lawrence with Henry Miller and Norman Mailer as prime examples of writers who celebrated the sexual exploitation, abuse and humiliation of women by men. Millett's polemical technique of selective quotation was particularly unfair to Lawrence, but there is no doubt that he did believe passionately that women should be passive and submissive in the sexual relationship and, like Freud, he disapproved of the clitoral orgasm. For all that, his work has probably done more good than harm to the cause of sexual happiness. Let us hope so, anyway, for *Lady Chatterley's Lover* is on every educated teenager's reading list.

So where, as Lawrence's centenary is celebrated in his native land with varying degrees of relevance (everything from a high-powered academic symposium at Nottingham University to a "D. H. Lawrence Centennial Half-Marathon Fun Run" around Eastwood) – where does Lawrence's reputation stand today?

My own impression is that, in the academic world, he is no longer the charismatic, controversial figure that once he was. Undergraduates are less likely to be turned on by his work than they were, and the days have passed when it seemed that every other postgraduate student wanted to do his or her thesis on Lawrence. The feminist critique has contributed to this effect, and so has the vogue for post-structuralist theory in literary studies (a writer whose work is so intensely personal, expressive and polemical as Lawrence's doesn't attract critics who maintain that the idea of the author is a fiction, a mere "function of discourse").

Personally, I find that this cooler, less partisan atmosphere is conducive to proper appreciation. As a student and young lecturer in the 50s and 60s I resisted the spell of Lawrence and the advocacy of his Leavisite admirers. A Londoner by birth and upbringing, I felt no immediate rapport with his provincialism, nor did his characteristic images of the green world of nature violated by black industry pierce me with the thrill of recognition. As a Roman Catholic, I was unmoved by his combination of puritan conscience and pagan pantheism. Leavis declared that one must be for Lawrence or for Joyce, one could not serve both masters. I was unreservedly a Joycean. I still am, but, like Anthony

Burgess, who describes a similar response in his very readable new study of Lawrence, *Flame into Being*, I no longer feel that admiration for one of these writers excludes the other.

In his own, less exuberantly experimental fashion, Lawrence was like Joyce a "polyphonic" novelist, to use a currently fashionable term coined by the Russian critic Mikhail Bakhtin to describe the art of Dostoevsky. Lawrence is the most Dostoevskian of English novelists, in whose best work conflicting ideological positions are brought into play and set against each other in a dialogue that is never simply or finally resolved. Even in his literary criticism, notably the remarkable *Studies in Classic American Literature*, Lawrence engages in dialogue not only with his readers but with his subjects, the dead writers.

That Lawrence himself is now a classic there is no doubt. A substantial sign of that status is the investment of Cambridge University Press in a superb edition of Lawrence's letters, which will eventually run to eight thick volumes, and a definitive edition of the author's complete works, claimed to be the "first edition of the whole canon of a classic modern author". Lawrence was rather casual about preserving the integrity of his own texts, and throughout his career they were subject to cuts and bowdlerizations with and without his knowledge. We are promised new versions of major novels like *Sons and Lovers* and *The Rainbow* that will be significantly different from and longer than the ones we know.

The Cambridge edition has already uncovered one treasure: the unfinished but substantial novel *Mr Noon*, written in 1920-1, only a small part of which was previously known to exist. It was published last year and shoddily treated by most English reviewers (Burgess was an honourable exception). Though disorganized and unpolished, it contains passages that only Lawrence could have written and that no living writer could equal. It permits one to relive the astonishment of Lawrence's first readers, and to understand why the word "genius" was so often on their lips.

The Human Nature of Narrative (1985)

I gave a public lecture in Canada recently at the end of which a man stood up and asked me a question. He had read a great many *Reader's Digest* "Condensed Books" and, when he had had occasion to make the comparison, they seemed to him just as good as, and sometimes better than, the original texts. If that were so, what was the point of all the matter that had been omitted from the condensed versions? My answer was the orthodox one: novels are narratives, but they are not *just* narratives – they have, or should have, other sources of interest and value. Certain kinds of popular fiction whose appeal was simply narrative might benefit by condensation, but I couldn't imagine that a novel like, say, *War and Peace* would lose nothing by being abridged.

I chose *War and Peace* as an example because it was the longest novel I could think of. I did not confess that, for the same reason, I haven't actually got around to reading it yet. My answer was disingenuous in other, more abstract ways. It implied an over-simplified model of the relationship between narrative and non-narrative elements in the novel. After all, it is not just the latter which are deleted from a "condensed" version of a given novel – some of the narrative content will almost certainly go too. Translations of novels to film provide the readiest examples. Take, for instance, *Great Expectations* – one of the texts discussed by Peter Brooks in his admirable new study of narrative.* In David Lean's highly praised film of 1946, the character of Orlick and all the action associated with him are omitted without any damage to the coherence and intelligibility of the story. This does not mean that Orlick

---

*P. Brooks, *Reading for the Plot: Design and Intention in Narrative* (Oxford University Press, 1984).

has no function in Dickens's text – he has, as Professor Brooks astutely observes, "throughout the novel acted as Pip's 'bad double', a hateful and sadistic version of the hero" – but it is not a necessary function. The Orlick subplot enriches the meaning of the text but is not essential to it. Pip's discovery that the former convict Magwitch is his benefactor, on the other hand, *is* essential. As Brooks says, "All the issues raised in the novel – social, ethical, interpretive – are here simultaneously brought to climax through the peripety of the plot." It is inconceivable that this piece of action could be deleted from any version of *Great Expectations*, even a hundred-word summary.

Jonathan Culler has observed that if you get a group of readers to summarize a novel or story in a specified number of words, they will invariably include and exclude the same data, suggesting that competent readers have an intuitive sense of what is and is not essential to narrative structure.* No one, I suppose, would claim that such a summary was an acceptable substitute for the text itself, though the logic of the "Condensed Books" enterprise might seem to point in that direction. What, then, is the difference between a condensation and a summary?

An answer to that question might begin with the Platonic distinction between *diegesis* (report of action) and *mimesis* (representation of action through the speech and gesture of actors). The plot summary of *Great Expectations* in *The Oxford Companion to English Literature* is pure diegesis; David Lean's film (apart from a few bits of voice-over narration) is pure mimesis. Dickens's text, like all novels, is a mixture of the two modes, of (to use modern terminology) "scene" and "summary", "showing" and "telling" – with a special complication inherent in all "first-person" narratives: Pip's diegetic report of his life includes mimesis of his own and other people's speech, but is itself a feat of mimesis on Dickens's part. *Great Expectations* is, in Mikhail Bakhtin's phrase, "doubly-voiced discourse". In the gaps between the narrating Pip and the narrated Pip, between Pip and his creator, meanings thrive and multiply. The impact of the film is more sensuously immediate but less complex. The impersonal plot summary is neither immediate nor complex. It is lifeless.

But not useless. To discuss a novel we have first to describe or recall its plot, however crudely and summarily. This suggests that plot (rather than, say, "character" or "theme" or "atmosphere") is the basic principle of cohesion in any novel, a truth rather neglected by modern Anglo-American criticism, including my own, until fairly recently. The reasons for this neglect were complicated† but certainly had much to

---

* J. Culler, "Defining Narrative Units", in *Style and Structure in Literature*, ed. Roger Fowler (Blackwell, 1975).

† They are discussed at greater length in the Afterword to a new edition of my *Language of Fiction* (Routledge & Kegan Paul. 1984; first published 1966).

do with the privileging of lyric poetry in the New Criticism and the downgrading of narrative in the critical pronouncements of the great modernist writers. E. M. Forster's weary concession, "Oh dear, yes, the novel must tell a story," Virginia Woolf's attacks on the well-plotted novels of Bennett and Wells, Conrad's defence of Henry James's open, inconclusive endings, T. S. Eliot's welcoming of Joyce's *Ulysses* ("instead of the narrative method, we may now use the mythical method") are all symptomatic of the modern suspicion of plot as something regressive, falsifying, and market-oriented, a suspicion that conveyed itself to modern academic criticism.

What changed the picture in the mid-60s was partly the foregrounding of narrative (often in new experimental ways) in post-modern fiction, and partly the critical discovery of continental European structuralism, which revealed a rich tradition of narratological theory going back to the Russian Formalists, with their seminal distinction between *fabula* (the story as it would have been enacted in real space/time) and *sjuzet* (the story as represented in a particular discourse). The New Criticism had managed only a stylistic purchase on fictional form. The work of Shklovsky, Propp, Todorov, Greimas, Genette and the early Barthes offered the possibility of a formalist critique of the novel that included plot – included, indeed, everything.

Everything, except, perhaps, an answer to the fundamental question: why do we, as human beings, apparently *need* narrative? What is it that impels us to tell and receive stories? What is it about the specifically novelistic realization of narrative that answers to the needs of a modern audience? These are the questions to which Professor Brooks addresses himself. While acknowledging the achievement of formalist narratology, and showing an easy familiarity with its methods and terminology, he believes that "it has too much neglected the temporal dynamics that shape narratives in our reading of them, the play of desire in time that makes us turn pages and strive towards narrative ends." The elegant four-term homologies of Lévi-Strauss and Greimas are satisfying to the analyst in their diagrammatic inclusiveness, but they hardly do justice to our actual experience of texts. Roland Barthes nudged structuralism in this direction with his influential essay of 1966, "Introduction to the Structural Analysis of Narratives", in which the narrative text is dissected into units that are classified as either *nuclei*, opening and closing possibilities for the characters, or *catalysers*, which fill up the spaces between the nuclei, and convey information about the characters, setting, etc. A nucleus cannot be deleted without damaging the coherence of a story, but catalysers are dispensable in this sense.

The model has an undeniable explanatory power, but it tends

inevitably to downgrade the importance of the catalysers (which make up the major part of any novel) and to make the reader a rather passive decoder of the narrative message. Significantly, Barthes took as his exemplary text Ian Fleming's *Goldfinger*, belonging to a genre in which the principle function of the catalysers is indeed simply that of postponing the resolution of narrative questions (thus creating suspense) while diverting the reader with information that is mildly interesting merely *as* information (technical, topographical, sexual, etc.). The model is incapable of explaining why we value *A Passage to India*, say, more than *Goldfinger*, or (it amounts to the same thing, but is not so easily brushed aside as bourgeois prejudice) why the former will bear rereading better than the latter. In trying to formulate a dynamic model for the transmission of narrative in the novel, Professor Brooks has taken a leaf or two out of Barthes's later work, *S/Z* (1970), a more elaborate analysis of a richer text (Balzac's "Sarrasine"); but above all he has been inspired by the writing of Sigmund Freud.

At the heart of all narrative there is a paradox, namely that the "end" of a story is both its goal and that which terminates the pleasure it yields. A story begins by arousing an expectation of its end (whether this is neatly closed or ambiguously open is less important than the "sense of an ending" itself), and it is the lure of this projected ending, continuously defined and modified by the narrative questions raised and (partially) resolved in the text, that draws us through its pages. We want to know "what happens". Yet in another sense we do not want to know – if we did, the plot summary would serve our purpose better than the text. We do not even want to be able to predict with certainty what will happen (hence the importance of peripety in all narrative of any sophistication). The postponement of satisfaction, in short, is essential to our enjoyment. Professor Brooks sees an analogy between this paradox and the operation of desire – especially, though not exclusively, sexual desire – as described in the Freudian (and Lacanian) account of the psyche: "a perpetual want for (of) a satisfaction that cannot be offered in reality." He is not the first to perceive this parallel: but no one, I believe, has explored it with such subtlety and perception, or illustrated it more persuasively. Furthermore, he has skilfully integrated the psychoanalytical model with other, more purely literary methods of analysis. *Reading for the Plot* is, indeed a book that restores one's faith in the future of academic criticism, because it shows that a writer can carry the whole freight of modern literary theory *lightly*, making use of it without being used by it.

For Brooks, the key Freudian text is *Beyond The Pleasure Principle* (1922), where Freud, starting with the enigma that shell-shocked patients from World War I tended to *repeat* rather than escape from their traumatic experiences in dreams, and pondering similar kinds of repetitious behaviour in "normal" life, came to question his previous belief that human beings are basically motivated by the desire for instinctual gratification, and formulated the daring hypothesis of a "death-instinct" – the idea that there is "an urge inherent in organic life to return to an earlier state of things" which is ultimately non-being. In short, "the ultimate aim of life is death", just as the aim of all narrative is to abolish itself in endings. Repetition in psychological life has a clear parallel in all the manifestations of equivalence in literary form, and both have similar functions.

Brooks seizes on Freud's description of this process as one of "binding" the energies of the primal instincts, and speculates:

> Repetition in all its literary manifestations may in fact work as a "binding" . . . of textural energies that allows them to be mastered by putting them into serviceable form . . . repetition, repeat, recall, symmetry, all those journeys back in the text, returns to and returns of, that allow us to bind one textual moment to another in terms of similarity or substitution rather than mere contiguity. Textual energy, all that is aroused into expectancy and possibility in a text, can become usable by plot only when it has been bound or formalized.

Behind this passage is an awareness, which Professor Brooks spells out elsewhere, of the relationship between metaphor and metonymy in narrative discourse. The import of a narrative is a "metaphoric" totalization of its meanings, a realization that its ending is the-same-as-but-different-from its beginning, but the route by which this goal is reached is a metonymic chain of temporal sequence and cause-and-effect.* The metonymic details can, however, acquire a quasimetaphoric force through the patterning (Forster called it "rhythm") that is the aesthetic equivalent of psychic "binding." In short, the "middle" of a novel is not just a mechanical device for postponing the resolution of its narrative questions, but an instructive, sense-making detour between the two silences that mark its beginning and its ending.

I must not give the impression that Professor Brooks's application of his Freudian model is ahistorical. The rise of the novel in the Enlightenment period to become the dominant literary form of the nineteenth century is related to the declining authority of the "providential plots" of revealed religion, History replacing Theology as the

---

* Metonymy is the trope by which A signifies B not by virtue of resemblance (as in metaphor) but by virtue of some spatio-temporal or logical contiguity. The distinction, classically formulated, and applied to the typology of discourse, by Roman Jakobson, is further explored in my *The Modes of Modern Writing* (1977).

privileged discourse through which human life is to be understood. The centrality of desire to the reading process is related to the prominence of plots of desire (sexual and material ambition) in the classic novels of the nineteenth century, such as those of Balzac and Stendhal. With the modern novel, self-consciousness and scepticism creep in, as early as Flaubert. Professor Brooks (who is Chairman of the Yale French Department) has a brilliant chapter on *L'Education sentimentale*, which shows how it alludes to yet deviates from the Balzacien novel. Ostensibly motivated by the desire for erotic and social success, Flaubert's hero recurrently displays a "problem in desire" – his will, or his nerve, fails him at every crucial moment, he is again and again pushed to the margin of events both private and public, and some of the most memorable passages in the book are shared between the reader and the author "over the head of the protagonist".

In the overtly experimental novels of modernist writers like Conrad (*Heart of Darkness*) and Faulkner (*Absalom, Absalom!*) the reliability of History as an explanatory discourse is brought into question, the lines between "fact" and "fiction" blur, and the transactive, collaborative nature of their relationship between narrator and narratee is foregrounded in the texts themselves. Freud's own writings display the same tendency, according to Brooks. The early classic case histories remind us strongly of the Sherlock Holmes stories, in which the genius of the detective/analyst solves the "crime" of neurotic symptoms by connecting together individually meaningless metonymic clues to form a sequence that leads back to the culprit of a childhood trauma. But when Freud admitted (as he did in the later additions to the case history of the Wolf Man) that the trauma might itself be a fiction constructed by the patient, he threw the whole psychoanalytic enterprise *en abîme*. No wonder Freud's ideas have been kept in currency by writers and literary critics rather than by scientists and doctors. The human need they satisfy is essentially the same as that served by every kind of narrative, from religious myths to novels. To say that is no insult to Freud, because, as Professor Brooks reminds us, narrative is one of the fundamental human tools for making sense of the world.

Rabbit Reviewer (1984)

"Our world of books, like most other worlds now, is the arena of an increasingly bitter struggle for space, and for the limited reading time that a busy citizen in this electronic age can afford." Thus John Updike, on page 877 of *Hugging the Shore*.* No, that page number is not a misprint: this collection of his occasional prose, mostly book reviews contributed to the *New Yorker* over the past eight years, runs to over nine hundred pages, including the index.

Is there not something paradoxical, you might ask, even inconsistent, about drawing attention to the problem of literary *Lebensraum* in a book which makes such a greedy claim on the reading public's time and energy? Updike seems to have included here every review he published since his last such collection, *Picked-up Pieces*, and has thrown in for good measure a number of journalistic items (including an unpublished squib that has been lingering in the files of the *New Yorker* since 1961), some lectures on classic American fiction, introductions to reprints of his own books, award-acceptance speeches, replies to questionnaires, and an interview with himself by his own fictional creation, Henry Bech. One would not be entirely surprised, by the end, to come across transcriptions of his marginal notes on all the other books he happened to read or re-read these past eight years.

"A man," opined Jane Austen's Mr John Knightley, when invited to dine with Mr Weston in late December, "must have a very good opinion of himself when he asks people to leave their own fireside and encounter such a day as this, for the sake of coming to see him. He must think himself a most agreeable fellow." And a man, we might think, in the

---

* J. Updike, *Hugging The Shore* (André Deutsch, 1984).

same crusty mood, must have a very high opinion of himself who would dump in the lap of the reading public, and on the desks of his fellow reviewers, an unabridged compendium of nearly a decade's fugitive literary journalism. Most readers of *Hugging the Shore*, whether they browse in it, or conscientiously turn every page, will, however, absolve the author of overweening vanity. He *is*, after all, like Mr Weston, an agreeable fellow (almost nothing in the book is dull or badly written); and, unlike Mr Weston, he is shrewdly and ironically aware of the presumptuousness of his enterprise. "Another book. Another slain forest. Another pious claim on our besieged pocketbooks," he sighs self-accusingly in his Foreword. "Even in the age of Ecclesiastes . . . the need for more books seemed doubtful." About writing the original reviews themselves, however, Updike is unapologetic:

> Book *reviews* perform a clear and desired social service: they excuse us from reading the books themselves. They give us literary sensations in concentrated form. They are gossip of a higher sort.

The very undiscriminating inclusiveness of this book makes it a fascinating record of a modern reviewer at work. I say "a" rather than "the", because Updike is not a wholly typical book reviewer. As a distinguished novelist, writing for a quality journal with which he has had a long and happy professional relationship (he was actually on the staff of *The New Yorker* for two years at the start of his literary career – and includes in this volume an evocative memoir of his apprenticeship on "Talk of the Town"), he enjoys a relatively privileged position – able, one supposes, to pick and choose his books, and to discuss them at much greater length than the average newspaper reviewer has at his disposal. Nevertheless, if one were asked to pick out a representative, non-specialist reviewer of our time, John Updike would be on most people's short-list. It is some time since John Gross pronounced the obsequies over the Man of Letters, but Updike has succeeded better than most in perpetuating that in many ways admirable profession – a profession in which there was always an essential quality of amateurism.

One cannot but be impressed by Updike's willingness to take on, as a reviewer, almost anything and anybody: not only American and English fiction, which one would expect, but also a wide range of foreign novelists – Jarry, Queneau, Céline, Pinget from France; Grass and Böll from Germany; Calvino from Italy; Lem and Shulz from Poland; Bely and Trifonov from Russia; Milan Kundera from Czechoslovakia; Sembèe Ousmane, Wole Soyinka, and T. Obinkaram Echewa from Africa; Natsume Sōseki, Junichirō Tanizaki and Shusako Endo from Japan – and not only fiction, but also poetry, folklore, anthropology, theology, travel, autobiography, literary criticism and art criticism. Rarely does he seem to be out of his depth, and on such occasions he turns his discomfiture to rhetorical advantage. From Roland Barthes' *S/Z* (an exhaustive semiotic analysis of Balzac's story, "Sarrasine"):

> the reader emerges, as from that imaginary machine of Kafka's which engraved commandments upon the transgressor's skin, lexically enriched, but lacerated; I cannot remember another book ostensibly in the English language which gave me such pains to peruse . . . [Barthes'] style is dense, tense, nervous, parenthetical, sometimes arch, and faintly insolent. He often seems to be recapitulating something we should have read but haven't.

This is so good that one can almost forgive Updike for getting Barthes' argument back to front: "Barthes insists . . . on the supremacy of 'readerly' (*lisible*) over 'writerly' (*scriptible*) literature." The reverse is actually the case.

That none of the *New Yorker's* numerous readers apparently wrote in to correct Updike on this point (as they did to correct other errors of fact in other reviews, acknowledged by Updike in footnotes to this book) is an interesting indication of how far Updike and his editors are prepared to range outside subjects known and familiar to that audience. Updike's claim that book reviews "excuse us from reading the books themselves" may sound flippant, and even cynical, but in fact it states an important truth.

Nobody can read all the books that lay claim to the attention of an educated man or woman. If it was ever possible (perhaps up to the end of the eighteenth century), it certainly isn't any longer. And it is a pedantic fallacy, or hypocrisy, to claim that only first-hand knowledge is real knowledge. Most people's knowledge of Darwin, Marx and Freud, arguably the three most important thinkers of the modern era, is second- or third-hand. Hence the importance of the generalist reviewer, to monitor and disseminate information about the endless production of new ideas and artefacts, on behalf of the rest of us, who will never have the time, opportunity or will to encounter them all directly.

The essential attributes for this kind of reviewing, in addition to intelligence and a liberal education, are an eye for the illuminating quotation and an easy, eloquent prose style. Possessing these qualifications, Updike is able to convey a vivid sense of the "feel" of a book, which one trusts. Sometimes the review will make one wish to read the book oneself – I felt this, for instance, in the case of his sensitive account of Shusako Endo's *Silence*, a book whose subject – the martyrdom of Christian missionaries in seventeenth-century Japan – does not seem inherently inviting. At other times – as with Calvino's 763-page collection of Italian folk-tales or Claude Lévi-Strauss's *The Origin of Table Manners*, or Edmund Wilson's journals – I was happy to let Updike take the strain of wading through these substantial volumes, and gratefully to accept his summaries and samples.

It goes without saying that a reviewer writing for a general audience must not only communicate clearly, but must seize and hold the reader's attention – all too apt to stray to the advertisements on the side of the page, or to turn the page in search of something more diverting – by a personal grace of style. But it is easy to overdo this. The more cramped the space at a reviewer's disposal, the more strained and intrusive such stylistic self-assertion is apt to seem. British book reviewers, in particular, are addicted to the pun, which combines condensation with rhetorical self-display.

John Updike's "gift for metaphorical elaboration" is so well known that he can refer to it himself in those words and wonder whether it was not "permanently overdeveloped" by his apprenticeship on *The New Yorker*. Because his reviews are fairly leisurely in pace, and not so anxious to impress as his novels (the American writer, Updike shrewdly observes, "feels called upon to perform miracles or to cease performing"), his gift for coining metaphors and similes enlightens and enlivens without cloying, as it sometimes does in the fictional prose. Consider, for example, two passages which employ basically the same figurative vehicle – broken glass – but apply it differently, and with discriminating precision in each case. Muriel Spark's novels, he suggests, "linger in the mind as brilliant shards, decisive as a smashed glass is decisive, evidence of unmistakable power rather casually applied"; while Milan Kundera's prose "presents a surface like that of a shattered mirror, whose brightly mirroring fragments lie mixed with pieces of lustreless silvering".

Another common and much-abused reviewer's ploy to get attention is to overdramatize the evaluative message of the review, indulging in either extravagant praise or cruel abuse in order to generate a vicarious excitement or *Schadenfreude* in the reader. Again, Updike avoids this vice. His praise is measured, and rarely unqualified; his criticisms slyly sardonic rather than sneering (Handke is "the complete child of modernism; Kierkegaard's absurdity, Sartre's nausea, was mother's milk to him"; the parting of two lovers in Gerthard Roth's *Winterreise* "occasions single-sentence paragraphs, an infallible sign of philosophical distress").

If Updike's reviews have a weakness it is the lack of an argumentative structure – the discursive equivalent of a plot – which many of them are long enough to invite and make one expect. He rarely seems to have a thesis to argue, or to make the review an occasion for offering a new and coherent view of a subject or author. None of these reviews would stand up as independent essays in their own right, like the classic review-articles of Eliot, Leavis, Trilling, and Edmund Wilson. They are essentially *reports*, made up of paraphrase, quotation, discrete reflections and *aperçus*; and they end rather suddenly, with somewhat empty rhetorical flourishes.

Reading *Hugging the Shore* gives one to think about book-reviewing as an institution, and its place in contemporary culture. An up-to-date study of this subject is greatly needed. In my own experience, most consumers of reviews are surprisingly ignorant of the process by which these discourses are generated and produced.

Many first-year students, I find, suppose that reviews are submitted, unsolicited, by those who write them. Few readers of this one need to be told that reviews are commissioned, usually with strict specifications as to length and deadline, by literary editors responsible for the book pages of newspapers and magazines. But how many know, for instance, that some reviewers are not paid *pro-rata* for each review, but receive a retainer (which may amount to a substantial salary) for supplying a regular review, on condition that they do not write for rival publications? Such retainers have provided a relatively secure base for many a literary career. Indeed, it is a fair assumption that most creative writers in Britain who do regular reviewing, whether as free-lances or on retainers, will earn more from this source, on a per-hour-of-work calculation, than they do from their novels and poems. This may not be true for a best-selling American writer like Updike, but his interesting admission in the Foreword to *Hugging the Shore*, that his monthly cheque from the *New Yorker* is almost exactly equivalent to his monthly alimony payment, suggests that it is not so far off the mark.

For the writer who is less obviously successful than Updike, reviewing as a source of regular income is a double-edged blessing. The writer cannot help resenting, occasionally, the time and energy taken away from his own work, to be spent on the work of others; and this resentment shows itself at times in irritable flashes of malice, or lazy, undiscriminating praise. Conversely, the reviewer who lavishes real compositional style and grace on his work is in some ways the most disinterested of literary perfectionists. Very few can hope, like John Updike, to see their reviews preserved between hard covers. Reviews are the butterflies of literary discourse, doomed to flutter brightly for a day or two, then to die and be forgotten.

Then there is the difficult and delicate matter of the reviewer's relationship with the other writers whom he may know and/or like and/or respect (or not), whom he may find himself reviewing and by whom he may himself have been reviewed in the past or expect to be reviewed in the future. Opening the book pages of our quality newspapers, the initiated reader will perceive in the apparently random conjunctions of reviewers and reviewed a network of connections invisible to the layman's eye. Reviewer A was at university with author B. Reviewer C has the same publisher or agent as author D. Reviewer E was once unfavourably reviewed by the present live-in lover of author F. And so on.

To draw attention to this fact is not to raise the old cry of a London literary mafia, a metropolitan conspiracy to control the literary market-place through internecine gang-warfare and the exclusion of new talent. On the whole one sees relatively few examples of flagrantly self-interested flattery or the settling of scores in today's book-reviewing. The pulled punch, the deliberately planted "puff" in an otherwise lukewarm review, are more common. Given the intense centralization and concentration of British literary life, such temptations to compromise are inevitable, and I couldn't claim to be totally blameless myself in this respect. A literary world that was totally disinfected, either by agreement or by decree, from such possible conflicts of interest would, in any case, be a very dull one. But some demystification of the whole machinery of book-reviewing would be healthy. What, for instance, about the role of literary editors, those *éminences grises* of the reviewing world, who choose the books to be reviewed, and match book to reviewer? The increasing commercialization of literary publishing (that is, the more intense and systematic application of accounting criteria to editorial policy, a development Updike comments caustically on more than once in his book) has correspondingly increased the power of, and pressures on, these men and women.

How far good reviews help, and bad reviews hinder, the sales of books is a subject of constant debate and disagreement in the publishing trade; but few would dispute that to be reviewed at all is better than to be ignored. Reviewing is a form of free advertisement, not in the sense of necessarily recommending the product, but of informing the potential buyer of its existence. Then there is the unquantifiable but crucial matter of the author's ego. It is difficult to retain faith in your work if the only feedback you get is from your friends and family. With the current overproduction of books of academic literary criticism, combined with the shrinking space for, and interest in, reviewing such books in newspapers and magazines, it is now quite common for very worthy books of this kind to be published and reviewed only, if at all, a year or two later, in those specialist academic journals whose bound volumes creak when you open them, like the doors of some seldom-visited church.

Updike is absolutely right: the Darwinian struggle for survival which governs literary discourse in an age not only of mechanical, but also of electronic reproduction, makes reviewing a cultural institution of crucial importance. Arguably, the function of reviewing, in *informing* ourselves of what is happening, is now more important than the evaluative function which has traditionally been seen as its *raison d'être*. Ironically, it is of the nature of reviews to add to the problem they address themselves to. Books breed like rabbits. This review of a book of reviews may one day appear in a book of my own, which will in turn be reviewed, and so on *ad infinitum*. The world does not need these books, but we need to write them. As Updike says to his self-created interrogator, Henry Bech, who taxes him on this point: "Print is guilt. Life is guilt. I believe it."

Tailpiece

Pillar Plant (1984)

Our house in Birmingham, a large Edwardian semi, has a side garden instead of a back garden, and my study window looks out on it. Like most writers, I spend a good deal of time gazing out of the window, and this garden view is familiar and soothing. Across the lawn there is a rockery, a laurel bush and a copper beech. There used to be, also, a small ivy-covered garden house overhung by a laburnum tree. The garden house was so rotten that it was held up mainly by the ivy, and the laburnum tree was splitting down the middle, having been used to secure one end of a washing line by the previous owners. My wife, who runs the horticultural side of our household, decreed last summer that these two ailing structures must go. The garden house was demolished, and the laburnum tree felled. The result, even after fresh turf had been laid, was an ugly and unsettling gap in the view from my study window, an absence that nagged away at my subconscious, a vacancy that cried out to be filled with some visual feature that would please without distracting. I decided that I would solve the problem, and contribute my mite to patronage of the arts, by buying a piece of modern sculpture for my garden.

Although I have bought the occasional contemporary painting or print, I had never before ventured into the world of three-dimensional art. I decided that I would pay a maximum of £300, though I hoped that I might get something I liked for less. This price bracket obviously meant that I would be looking at work by young, comparatively unknown sculptors, perhaps even students. I phoned up the Fine Arts officer of West Midlands Arts and explained my need. She was most helpful, and immediately gave me a list of local sculptors who worked in materials suitable for outdoor display. One name, Rosemary Terry, particularly attracted my attention, because she had apparently just had a piece bought for the Chelsea Gardens, Telford – a prize-winning sculpture park in the town centre.

The following Saturday, a sunny, breezy day in September, my wife and I drove over to Telford. It's a New Town in Shropshire, about forty miles north-west of Birmingham, and the town centre consists mainly of a huge enclosed shopping centre, of futuristic design, and an immense car park, filled that afternoon by anxious-faced shoppers. None of them had heard of the Chelsea Gardens. Some, indeed, scarcely seemed to know where they were. "I'm a stranger here myself," said one lady whom my wife accosted – adding, as if suddenly awakening from a trance, "No, I'm not, I live here. But I can't help you, sorry."

Eventually we had to go to the police station, where we were directed to the town park, a windswept hill overlooking the shopping centre. And there, sure enough, on the far side of the hill, enclosed in a high wooden fence, were the Chelsea Gardens: an enchanting complex of flower-beds, shrubs, fishponds, arbours, summerhouses and sculptures. In one corner, beside a small Japanese pagoda, we found Rosemary Terry's sculpture, entitled "Pillar Plant." A vertical hexagonal form, about five feet high, and a foot across at its widest point, smoothly carved from pale honey-coloured stone, it was well named, for it combined the sinuous organic shape of vegetation with the geometric precision and solidity of architecture. It was exactly the sort of thing I had been hoping to find, and if it had been for sale I should have taken it home with me.

Since it was not, I telephoned Rosemary Terry at her Wolverhampton studio. She told me that she was going to have an exhibition at a small gallery in nearby Tettenhall in October, and invited me and my wife to the private view. Among the exhibits we found an earlier and slightly smaller version of Pillar Plant. It did not have quite the classical purity and elegance that characterized the Chelsea Gardens piece; it was carved from coarser, softer stone (sandstone, in fact) and instead of having a smooth polished, hexagonal surface, it was cylindrical in shape and textured with wrinkly lines and indentations. But it had the same pleasing sinuousness – the serpentine line of beauty, as the eighteenth-century painters called it – that hesitated intriguingly between the organic and the artificial. And it was remarkably cheap: £120. I bought it.

Rosemary, a shy, slightly-built young woman, scarcely looked strong enough to handle her own artefacts; but Pillar Plant I (as it was called in the catalogue) was composed of four sections, balanced one on top of the other. For safety and durability, we agreed that they would have to be joined together with dowelling and adhesive when the piece was installed in my garden (I didn't have third-party insurance against collapsing sculpture). My builder installed a concrete plinth, with projecting pieces of steel dowelling placed according to a template supplied by Rosemary. Some precision was required in this matter, since I required the sculpture to be placed so as to present the full profile of its sinuous curve to my view from the study window. In November, when the exhibition was over, Rosemary brought the four sections over to Birmingham and erected the sculpture in my garden. I never made a better bargain.

Of course, Pillar Plant is not to everybody's taste. It has been jocularly likened to an elephant's knee, a friendly triffid, a gnome from outer space, a thwarted bird-bath, a monument to the Unknown IRA Informer. But *I* like it. As I perceived when I first set eyes on the Telford version, it visually echoes the shape of the copper beech behind it. Its colour-tone varies with the seasons, the weather, and the time of day: grey in the rain, glistening white in the frost, creamy in the afternoon sun. In winter the snow clings to its textured surface in a windshaped ridge that highlights its sinuous curve. On spring mornings a snail's shining mucous thread sometimes traverses its flanks. In summer it hovers behind the garden table like a deferential waiter, its flat top a convenient resting-place for a cup or glass. At night it glimmers ghost-like in the dark, disconcerting prowlers. Looking up from my desk, gazing out of my window, I never tire of it. Its silent form teases me out of thought.

> *When old age shall this generation waste,*
> *Thou shalt remain, in midst of other woe*
> *Than ours, a friend to man, to whom thou say'st*

– well, perhaps not all ye know on earth and all ye need to know, but certainly that owning your own sculpture is a lot of fun.

[*Postscript*: Since this was written we have moved house, but we took Pillar Plant with us. It seems to be quite happy in the walled patio on which my new study looks.]

The Tortoise's Gift

A Story from Zambia

Retold by Lari Don • Illustrated by Melanie Williamson

Barefoot Books
step inside a story

Contents

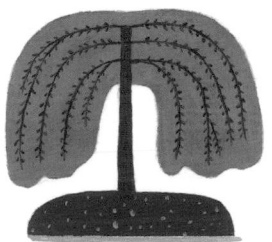

The
Tortoise's
Gift

As always, for Colin, Mirren and Gowan — L. D.

For Reuben, love from Auntie Mels x — M. W.

Barefoot Books
2067 Massachusetts Avenue
Cambridge, MA 02140

Series Editor: Gina Nuttall
Text copyright © 2012 by Lari Don
Illustrations copyright © 2012 by Melanie Williamson
The moral rights of Lari Don and
Melanie Williamson have been asserted

First published in the United States of America by
Barefoot Books, Inc in 2012
All rights reserved

Graphic design by Helen Chapman, West Yorkshire, UK
Cover design by Penny Lamprell, Hampshire, UK
Reproduction by B&P International, Hong Kong
Printed in China on 100% acid-free paper
This book was typeset in Tractor, Classy Diner and Bembo Infant
The illustrations were prepared in acrylic, pencil and chalk

Thank you to Y2 at St Anne's Catholic Primary School, Caversham, UK
for all their careful reading

Sources:
Umansky, Kaye. *Three Singing Pigs:
Making Music with Traditional Stories*. A & C Black, London, 2005.

ISBN 978-1-84686-774-3

Library of Congress Cataloging-in-Publication Data
is available under LCCN 2011032859

3 5 7 9 8 6 4

The Wonderful Tree

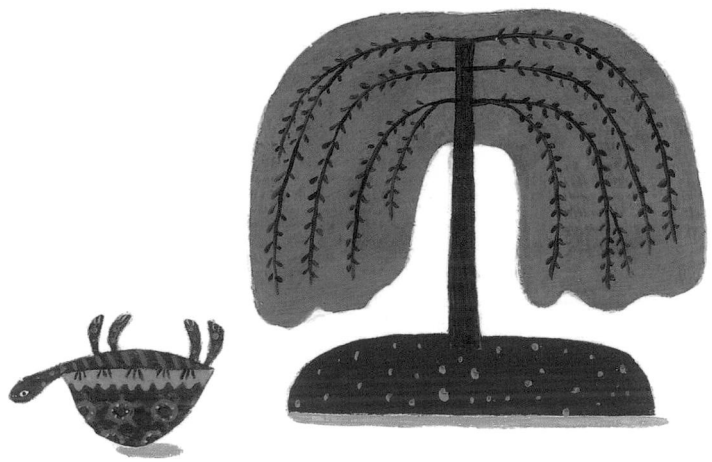

One hot, dry summer in Zambia, the rain stopped falling. Soon the rivers stopped flowing and the grass stopped growing. Soon the animals were very thirsty and very hungry.

The old rabbit had heard stories about a wonderful tree in the middle of the forest. He told the other animals, "When the rain stops falling, this wonderful tree grows every animal's favorite fruit. So no animal is ever hungry or thirsty."

The animals searched the middle
of the forest and found a strange
tree. It was not a palm tree or a
baobab tree or a banana tree. The
animals did not know what kind of
tree it was. So they thought it must
be the wonderful tree.

But it looked old and tired and
thirsty, just like all the other trees in
the forest. It looked like it would not
wake up and grow anything until
the rains came back.

"There isn't any fruit on it," said
the elephant.

"Maybe we have to tell it what
our favorite fruit is," said the chimps.

So they all shouted loudly: "Give
me bananas!", "I want grapes!", "Give
me mangoes!", "I want pineapple!"

But the tree did not grow any fruit. The lion said, "Maybe there's a magic word."

"I know what the magic word is," squeaked a baby monkey. "My mommy says the magic word is 'please'."

Please!

So they all shouted:
"Bananas, please!"
"Mangoes, please!"
But the tree did not
grow any fruit.

"Maybe it doesn't know we're talking to it," said the monkey's mom. "Maybe it thinks we're asking the banana trees for bananas and the mango trees for mangoes."

"So let's call it by its name," suggested the chimps.

"Good idea," said the elephant. "What is its name?"

CHAPTER 2

What is the Tree's Name?

Um...

No one knew the tree's name. No one had needed the tree for a long, long time. So now, no one could remember its name.

"Who is old enough to remember the tree's name?" wondered the animals.

"What about the mountain?"
said the chimps.

They all looked up and saw the
mountain beyond the forest. It was
pointing up to the sky.

"The mountain has been here
longer than the grass or the trees.
The mountain will know!" they all
agreed.

But the mountain was on the
other side of the grasslands. It was
far away and the animals were all
tired and thirsty and hungry.
"Who will go and ask the
mountain?" they all asked.

The lion stepped forward. He said, "I will go! I am the bravest, so I will go. But I want the first pick of the fruit when I bring back the name."

The other animals agreed that was fair.

Me!

So the lion crossed the grasslands
in his quiet, creeping way.

He reached the foot of the huge,
rocky mountain and looked up.

"Mountain, can you please tell
me the name of the wonderful tree
in the middle of the forest?" he asked.

The mountain rumbled,
"AWONGALEMA."

The lion bowed. He said, "Thank
you," and he started back across the
grasslands.

The lion was very pleased with
himself. What a famous hero he
would be!

19

He would bring back the name
of the tree. Then he would wake up
the tree and feed all the animals!

He reached the big red rock
halfway across the grasslands. He
was so pleased with himself that he
decided to stop for a nice big…

Roar!

He stood in the shadow of the rock, roaring his loudest. And he roared the name right out of his head!

21

The lion went slowly back to the other animals. They were waiting in a hungry circle around the tree.

The animals asked, "So, what is the name? Did the mountain tell you? What is the tree's name?" The lion was embarrassed. Very quietly, he said, "I forgot…"

CHAPTER 3

Who Will Try Next?

The animals wondered who else
could go to the mountain. Who else
could bring the name all the way back?

The elephant stepped forward.
He said, "I will go. I am the biggest,
so I will go."

The other animals thought that
was a very good idea. The elephant
had a very big head, with lots of
space to remember the name.

They agreed that, if the elephant
brought the name back, he could
have first pick of the fruit.

So the elephant crossed the
grasslands in his loud, stomping way.

He reached the foot of the huge,
rocky mountain, and looked up.

"Mountain, please tell me the name
of the wonderful tree in the middle of
the forest?" he asked.

The mountain rumbled,
"AWONGALEMA."

The elephant raised his trunk in
salute. He said, "Thank you," and he
started back across the grasslands.

The elephant was very pleased
with himself. What a famous hero
he would be!

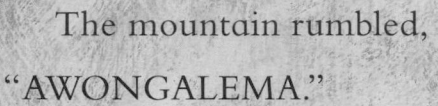

He would bring back the name
of the tree. Then he would wake up
the tree and feed all the animals!

He reached the big red rock
halfway across the grasslands. He
was so pleased with himself that he
decided to stop for a nice, long…

Scratch!

He rubbed his wrinkly hide up against the rock. And he scratched the name right out of his head!

The elephant went slowly back
to the other animals. They were
waiting in a hungry circle around
the tree. The animals asked, "So,
what's the name? Did the mountain
tell you? Can you remember the
tree's name?"

The elephant was embarrassed.
Very quietly, he said, "I forgot…"

CHAPTER 4

The Playful
Chimps

The animals wondered who else
could go to the mountain. Who else
could get the name and remember
it and bring it all the way back?

The chimps jumped up and
down. They said, "We will go. We
are the cleverest, so we will go."

The other animals thought that
was a very good idea. After all, the
chimps were very clever. They used
tools and they chattered all the time.
They were so clever that they would
certainly remember the name.

The other animals agreed that, if the chimps brought the name back, they could have first pick of the fruit.

So the chimps crossed the grasslands in their bouncy, chattering way.

They reached the foot of the huge, rocky mountain, and looked up. "Mountain, can you please tell us the name of the wonderful tree in the middle of the forest?" they asked.

The mountain rumbled, "AWONGALEMA."

The chimps clapped their hands. They said, "Thank you," and they started back across the grasslands. The chimps were very pleased with themselves. What famous heroes they would be!

Hooray! Hooray!

They would bring back the
name of the tree. Then they would
wake up the tree and feed all the
animals!

They reached the big red rock
halfway across the grasslands. They
were so pleased with themselves
that they decided to stop and have
some…

Fun!

They jumped off the rock and they tickled each other. And they tickled the name right out of their heads!

The chimps went slowly back to the forest. The other animals were waiting in a hungry circle around the tree. The animals asked, "So what's the name? Did you listen carefully? What is the tree's name?"

The chimps were embarrassed. Very quietly, they said, "We forgot…"

Sorry.

CHAPTER 5

Slow and Steady

The animals stood hungry and thirsty around the wonderful tree. It still had not fed them. They wondered who could bring back the name now.

A little voice said, "I will go."

The animals looked up and they looked around, but they could not see who had spoken.

The voice said again, "I will go." So the animals looked down. It was the tortoise.

"You can't go," said the animals. "You are too small and you are far too slow. You won't get the name and, even if you do, you'll never bring it back."

But the tortoise said, "I will go." And he did. He crossed the grasslands in his slow, steady way, one step at a time.

Finally, he reached the foot of the huge, rocky mountain, and looked up. "Excuse me, Mountain, can you please tell me the name of the wonderful tree in the middle of the forest?" he asked.

Thank you.

The mountain rumbled, "AWONGALEMA."

The tortoise said, "Awongalema. Is that right?"

The mountain smiled and nodded.

So the tortoise thanked the
mountain, and started back across
the grasslands. He went slowly and
steadily, one step at a time.

As he stepped, he chanted,
"A – WON – GA – LE – MA."

The tortoise did not feel pleased
with himself. The tortoise did not hope
he would be famous. He just said,
"A – WON – GA – LE – MA."

The tortoise did not stop at the big red rock. He did not roar or scratch or tickle. He just kept going, slowly and steadily, one clawed foot at a time, saying:

"A – WON – GA – LE – MA."

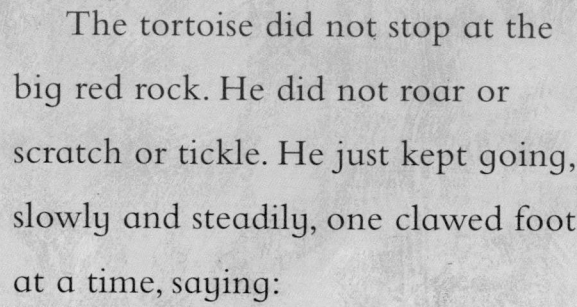

The tortoise finally reached the
hungry circle of animals around the
tree. He looked up at the tree and
said, "Awongalema, will you please
wake up and feed us all?"

The tree shivered and its branches creaked. Its tiny leaves grew wide and green. Its little hard buds blossomed into big, bright flowers. As the animals watched, the petals fell.

44

The centers of the flowers swelled and grew into all their favorite fruit: bananas, grapes, mangoes and pineapples! Once the fruit had ripened for a moment in the sun, it fell gently to the dry ground.

Every animal in the circle waited politely for the tortoise to step forward. Slowly, steadily, one clawed foot at a time, the tortoise walked toward his favorite fruit.

46

He opened his mouth wide and took the first bite. It was the most delicious, the most refreshing, the juiciest…

…red grape he had ever eaten! The tortoise ate the whole bunch, slowly and steadily, one red grape at a time.

Yum!